Six of the Best

A Puffin Sextet of Poets

Chosen and introduced by Anne Harvey

PUFFIN BOOKS

PUFFIN BOOKS

Published by the Penguin Group
27 Wrights Lane, London W8 5TZ, England
Viking Penguin Inc., 40 West 23rd Street, New York, New York 10010, USA
Penguin Books Australia Ltd, Ringwood, Victoria, Australia
Penguin Books Canada Ltd, 2801 John Street, Markham, Ontario, Canada L3R 1B4
Penguin Books (NZ) Ltd, 182–190 Wairau Road, Auckland 10, New Zealand

Penguin Books Ltd, Registered Offices: Harmondsworth, Middlesex, England

This collection first published 1989
10 9 8 7 6 5 4 3 2 1

Filmset in Monophoto Photina

Made and printed in Great Britain by
Richard Clay Ltd, Bungay, Suffolk

To the memory of
WALTER DE LA MARE
1873–1956

The children who explored the brook and found
A desert island with a sandy cove . . .
Recount their exploits at the nursery tea

And when the lamps are lit and curtains drawn
Demand some poetry, please. Whose shall it be,
At not quite time for bed? . . .

from *To Walter de la Mare* by T. S. Eliot

Contents

ALAN BROWNJOHN

PHOEBE HESKETH

Preface

I was doing a poetry reading in a school one day when a child asked me: 'What is a dedication?' Another child answered for me: 'It's a sort of sacrifice.' Not quite, perhaps, but it is a way of giving, or offering, a book to someone you respect. *Poets in Hand: A Puffin Quintet of Poets* was dedicated to the memory of Eleanor Farjeon, and I felt I would like *Six of the Best* to be similarly dedicated to her great friend, Walter de la Mare. He was the first poet I was really aware of, and the very first poem I learnt by heart was the 'The Cupboard' from his *Peacock Pie*. I knew that Leonard Clark had made a special study of de la Mare and written a book about him. Then I discovered that both Alan Brownjohn and Russell Hoban had dedicated poems to him, that Brian Lee and Phoebe Hesketh admired his work very much, and that George Barker had known and loved him. So it is with the approval of everyone involved that this dedication is made.

The six poets in *A Puffin Sextet of Poets* have been chosen because of their individual tone and style, because they have something to say in poetry that is sad, or true, or funny, or interesting, and because they don't write in a condescending way 'for children'.

Walter de la Mare once gave this advice to children: 'We can ... and particularly when we are young, delight in the sound of the words of a poem, immensely enjoy them – the music and rhythm and lilt, feel its enchantment and treasure it in memory, without realizing its full meaning ... It is best to find your way in a poem for yourself.'

GEORGE BARKER

... George Granville Barker was born in Essex in 1913 of an English father and Irish mother, and educated at the Marlborough Road School, Chelsea, and (briefly) at the Regent Street Polytechnic. In 1939 he taught in a Japanese University, and then lived in America and Canada from 1940 to 1943. After this he returned to England, though he lived and worked for further periods in America and Italy.

His published work includes *Thirty Preliminary Poems* (David Archer, 1933), *Poems* (1935), *Calamiterror* (a semi-political poem inspired by the Spanish Civil War, 1937), *Lament and Triumph* (1940), *Eros in Dogma* (1944), *The True Confession of George Barker* (1950), *News of the World* (1950), *A Vision of Beasts and Gods* (1954), *The View from a Blind* (1962), *Dreams of a Summer Night* (1966), *The Golden Chains* (1968), *Poems of Places and People* (1971), *In Memory of David Archer* (1973), *Dialogues, etc* (1976), *Villar Stellar* (1978), *Anno Domini* (1983), *Collected Poems* (1987), all published by Faber and Faber.

His poetry for children includes *Runes and Rhymes and Tunes and Chimes* (1969), *To Aylsham Fair* (1970) and *The Alphabetical Zoo* (1972), all published by Faber and Faber.

The poems in this selection are taken from *Runes and Rhymes and Tunes and Chimes*, *To Aylsham Fair* and *Collected Poems*.

When the presenter, Melvyn Bragg, introduced George Barker on ITV's *South Bank Show* in 1988, he said: 'There is no one in England who has a better claim to put the word poet on his passport.'

Poetry began early for George Barker. He can recall his mother reciting Walter Scott's:

> O hush thee, my babie, thy sire was a knight,
> Thy mother a ladie both gentle and bright.

His Irish mother had run away from home, her head filled with the poems she had memorized at school. She was a tremendous personality whom many still remember and talk about. George introduced her to a wider public in his sonnet 'To My Mother'.

George's early childhood was spent in Chelsea in a block of tenement flats called the Samuel Lewis Trust Buildings:

> . . . and over those years, for me, and for my brother
>   and sisters
> the spectre, worse than the spectre of war over
>   Europe,
> of my parents' poverty. My mother every Wednesday
>   pawning her wedding ring
> and the blanket from her bed . . . my father returning
>   at evening
> to the three small tenement rooms and his family of
>   seven,
> a twist of drawn exhaustion on his face . . .

3

When George was about thirteen his mother somehow managed to scrape enough money together to buy him a huge, second-hand typewriter from Selfridges, and on this he banged out his first poems.

The school he went to in Chelsea was 'old and Dickensian, enormous and wonderful, a huge menagerie. I loved it ... it was a tough school.' But he didn't love the headmaster, George Sampson, who had once edited a history of literature, and was 'so distinguished that he knew it ... a horrible man!' Years later Sampson wrote to George, 'How could you have possibly written any verse; you were a very very undistinguished little boy!' This delighted George who wouldn't have wanted to be liked by him. He much preferred a teacher called Miss Christie, who taught that there were nice things in the world as well as nasty, and who read Scottish ballads aloud to the boys.

George was good at football, and told me he once played for Chelsea. I was most impressed, thinking he meant the well-known team ... 'For the Chelsea Schools,' he said. 'You're very ignorant about football.' I admitted it, then went on to show worse ignorance about boxing, another of his loves. Nowadays George is an avid watcher of sport on television. In fact I had strict instructions to visit him 'after the wrestling, before the football'.

The first poet he really adored was the Elizabethan, Edmund Spenser – he loved the long elaborate poem 'The Faerie Queene'. Other poets he admired included Tennyson, A. E. Housman and W. H. Auden. While still in his teens, he realized that he 'could make things happen by writing about them, and from that moment on was a sucker for it'.

4

His father thought he was wasting his time and wanted his sons to have proper, secure jobs. (George's brother, Kit, became an artist, but by the age of sixteen George felt he was a great poet and so dressed for the part in an ankle-length blue cloak and a huge Spanish-style hat – looking exactly the advertisment for Sande-man's Port. George had been a week in the office of a chartered accountant, when his employer said: 'This is no good . . . I refuse to employ a young man who looks like an out-of-work violinist . . . you're sacked!')

Through a London bookseller, David Archer, he met other writers, and was advised to send his poems to Walter de la Mare. He did, they met and got on well. One day there was a sudden thunderstorm, and de la Mare said, 'Never forget the thunderstorm, George.' And he never has. He told George that his verse was 'fine and dandy', but he didn't quite follow the kind of material he was writing, so he gave him a letter of introduction to T. S. Eliot at Faber. He was twenty-two when Eliot published his poems.

The writer, Paul Potts, said, 'George Barker's beginning was a triumph . . . His world . . . is populated with people he has loved and crowded with people who love him . . . The man is a poet and he has made his poems out of his life.'

Having chosen George Barker as one of the six poets to be included in this collection, I set out to read far more of his poetry, for adults and children, than I already knew. I was overwhelmed not by the amount, but the variety, the range of pattern, the joy and sorrow, the lyrical and surrealistic . . . somehow what I can only describe as the huge, pulsing effect of it.

Meeting George I thought him kind and welcoming,

5

extrovert and blunt, with a sharp sense of humour. He loathes politics and politicians. I found him more inclined to answer a child's letter querying 'What was the rarest animal in the world?' than one from a 'boring autograph hunter'.

For more than twenty years he has lived with Elspeth and their five children in a very beautiful old house rented from the National Trust, near Aylsham, north Norfolk. It's an atmospheric house with a sense of the past, but essentially comfortable and inviting, the walls covered with books and pictures, the gardens well cared for yet informal, horses in a field, a nearby river. Important members of the household are T-Shirt Smith and Honey, black and gold labradors; five cats (whose names I didn't learn) and the few remaining of their recent litters of kittens.

I heard about Ginger, the cat in 'Death of a Cat', who disappeared for three months before returning three-legged. And George told me how his children often gave him ideas. It was Raffaella who invented the character Dibby Dubby Dhu. I thought this might be his 'other self' . . . he raised his hands and said in a teasing way: 'Who knows?' He says he has not yet fulfilled an ambition to write a children's story called 'Queen La Dancing Umbrella'.

George Barker has now been writing for over fifty years. 'If I didn't write poetry,' he said, 'I would explode.'

Introduction

'And what,' said the Emperor, 'does this poem describe?'
  'It describes,' said the Poet, 'the Cave of the Never-
  Never.'
'Would you like to see what's inside?' He offered his
  arm.
  They stepped into the poem and disappeared for ever.

In Foggy Dawns

In foggy dawns
as cold as yawns,
in pitch black nights
when no moon lights
familiar sights
as she rides the rolling sky,
in kitchen, garden and in attic,
as though my pen was automatic
I make these rhymes
and tunes and chimes
for several children. Why?
Because my head
is like a bed
from which at times
these runes and rhymes
get up and start to fly.
They whiz about
both in and out
they make my room so cluttered
(as if I fell
down a wishing well
and all the wishes fluttered).
These runes and rhymes
and tunes and chimes
like gnomes and elves
disport themselves
on my bookshelves
in fours and eights
and tens and twelves
until I think that I'll

have neither chair,
chamber or stair
(and I've got many)
or table where
I can find any
room to spare,
for they'll be there
these rhymes like gnomes
these runes like elves
I make for children. I
think I shall run a mile.

Should I Ever Again Meet

Should I ever again meet
   the white horse that
I once saw in Harrogate
   wearing a straw hat,
well, if I wore mine then,
   (and I sometimes do)
I would raise it in the street
   as a matter of course
   in order to greet
   that Harrogate horse,
my friend, that be-hatted, sorrow-faced,
   Harrogate horse.

Never, My Love and Dearest

Never, my love and dearest,
   we'll hear the lilies grow
or, silent and dancing,
   the fall of the winter snow,
or the great clouds of Summer
   as on their way they go.

Never, my love and dearest,
   we'll hear the bluebells chime
or the whole world turn over
   after the starlit time.
O not everything, my dearest,
   needs to be said in rhyme!

This Is a Rune
I Have Heard a Tree Say

This is a rune I have heard a tree say:
'Love me. I cannot run away.'

This is a rune I have heard a lark cry:
'So high! But I cannot reach the sky.'

This is a rune I have heard a dog bark:
'I see what is not even there in the dark.'

This is a rune I have heard a fish weep:
'I am trying to find you when I leap.'

This is a rune I have heard a cat miaow:
'I died eight times so be kind to me now.'

This is a rune I have heard a man say:
'Hold your head up and you see far away.'

On a Sunday Evening

On a Sunday evening
we came to Swanton Nevers
on our bicycles;
it was a dark December
and even the white signpost
dripped with icicles.

My sister's name is Mary.
She rides a rather shaky
camel of a bike.
And at Swanton Nevers
that December evening
It went on strike.

I hit it, I bit it,
I stroked it, I poked it,
still it would not go.
It lay there like
a camel bike
frozen to death in snow.

And so of Swanton Nevers
(with a name like that it
ought to be a summer
Paradise-by-Thames)
And so of Swanton Nevers
I shall always think with
dees and ayes and ems.

My Sister Clarissa Spits Twice if I Kiss Her

My sister Clarissa spits twice if I kiss her
and once if I hold her hand.
I reprimand her – my name's Alexander –
for spitting I simply can't stand.

'Clarissa, Clarissa, my sister, is this a
really nice habit to practise?'
But she always replies with innocent eyes
rather softly, 'Dear Brother, the fact is

I think I'm an ape with a very small grape
crushed to juice in my mastodon lips.
Since I am not a prude, though I hate being rude,
I am simply ejecting the pips.'

Mary-in-the-Garden

Mary-in-the-Garden
who are you talking to?
O Mother, it is my brother Peter
I am talking to.

Mary-in-the-Garden
who are you walking with?
O Mother, it is my brother Peter
I am walking with.

How can that be, my Mary?
O how can that ever be?
Your brother Peter is far, far away
over the widest sea.

Mother, the sea he is over
No ship ever sails,
no sun ever shines there
and no wind stirs the gales.

He sleeps in those far islands, Mother,
so far that no ship or
bird ever rested by
that dark and farewell shore.

O Mary-in-the-Garden
then how can he walk with you?
O Mary-in-the-Garden
how can he talk with you?

In the Garden, in the evening,
said Mary to her Mother,
he comes to me over that sea,
My Peter, my Brother.

To My Mother

Most near, most dear, most loved and most far,
Under the window where I often found her
Sitting as huge as Asia, seismic with laughter,
Gin and chicken helpless in her Irish hand,
Irresistible as Rabelais, but most tender for
The lame dogs and hurt birds that surround her –
She is a procession no one can follow after
But be like a little dog following a brass band.

She will not glance up at the bomber, or condescend
To drop her gin and scuttle to a cellar,
But lean on the mahogany table like a mountain
Whom only faith can move, and so I send
O all my faith, and all my love to tell her
That she will move from mourning into morning.

For the Fourth Birthday
of My Daughter

When she opens her eye this morning
    upon her fourth year
    may every fruit and flower
    may every bird and beast
    may every herb and tree
    may every child and every
    holy infant hour
seem in bright presence here
    to exercise this day
    their beneficient power
    so that around her bed
    they stand in clusters and
    choirs hand in hand
singing her welcome here
    and every bright-eyed stellar
    and sub-stellar order
    gather around to tell her
    all is created for her
    all for Raffaella
    Raffaella Flora.

O Child Beside the Waterfall

O Child beside the Waterfall
what songs without a word
rise from those waters like the call
only a heart has heard –
the Joy, the Joy in all things
rise whistling like a bird.

O Child beside the Waterfall
I hear them too, the brief
heavenly notes, the harp of dawn,
the nightingale on the leaf,
all, all dispel the darkness and
the silence of our grief.

O Child beside the Waterfall
I see you standing there
with waterdrops and fireflies
and hummingbirds in the air,
all singing praise of paradise,
paradise everywhere.

They Call to One Another

They call to one another
    in the prisons of the sea
the mermen and mermaidens
    bound under lock and key
down in the green and salty dens
    and dungeons of the sea,
lying about in chains but
    dying to be free:
and this is why shortsighted men
    believe them not to be
for down to their dark dungeons it
    is very hard to see.

But sometimes morning fishermen
    drag up in the net
bits of bright glass or the silver comb
    of an old vanity set
or a letter rather hard to read
    because it is still wet
sent to remind us never, never
    never to forget
the mermen and mermaidens
    in the prisons of the sea
who call to one another
    when the stars of morning rise
and the stars of evening set
    for I have heard them calling
and I can hear them, yet.

She Lies by the Island of Spices and Zephyrs

She lies by the Island of Spices and Zephyrs
where the monkeys play hide and seek up in old trees
and the humming-birds balance all day on a single
blade of tall grass as it sways in the breeze.

There the gold fish blow bubbles among water lilies
simply to pass the time of the day
and high on the mountain the summer cloud lingers
rather than pass on its heavenly way.

She lies there and roses climb out of her portholes
the juniper trails from her f'castle down,
at her figurehead glitters the eye of the basilisk
like the sea-green jewel of a gold crown.

She lies there, rock riven, her mizzen mast shattered
and the seaweeds garb her all over in green.
Who was she? Who knows? Who knows? No one.
The name on her side will never be seen.

from *Dreams of a Summer Night*

I think of her where she lies there on her stone couch by
    the Thames
With the winds of the world asleep among her shrouds
    and the gales
Hushed in her furled sails and the pawing white
    seahorses
At last at rest around her and the mermen of yesterday
    calling to her
From the wind tossed reach of the river as it sweeps
    through Greenwich
Meridian. I think of her as I think of a seagull caged in
    chains but
Still standing poised, prepared, wings lifted, for the rise
    and veer
Into the sunrise of Asia as far as the paradise islands of
The Coral Sea. And below her decks all the great
    figure-heads fraternizing
Like kings and queens at a feast – Cleopatra, the
    Lallah Rookh,
Abraham Lincoln, Thermopylae, the American Officer,
Diana and Marianne, filling her hold with the dialogues
Of storms and calms, of long summer days and seas
Murmuring in their dreams, all these join with the voices
Of the dead sailor still roped at the chained wheel and
The ghosts that lean singing into the bitter wind that
    drives up from
The thundering graves of the sea.

I Last Saw Dibby Dubby Dhu

I last saw Dibby Dubby Dhu
  sitting in a cave
washing his dirty shirts and socks
  in every seventh wave.

The clay pipe in between his teeth
  like an irate volcano
puffed out huge clouds of smoke that roared
  loud as a hurricano.

His eye flashed fire all about
  the rocks and wild sea lodges
like the forked lightning when it strikes
  and everybody dodges.

He was, I saw, a Castaway
  upon an unknown shore
the sole survivor of a ship
  that sails the seas no more.

It was not in a dream or in
  a magic crystal ball
I saw him sitting by that cave
  with no one else at all.

But as to far-off Africa
  in a great plane I flew
I looked down on those desolate seas
  and there, below, stood Dhu.

He lifted up his searchlight eyes
   as I looked down on him
when, lo! he did a perfect dive
   and he began to swim.

I see it all before me now
   clear as I saw it then –
Castaway Dhu's return unto
   the Living World of Men!

You Many Big Ships With Your Billowing Sails

You many big ships with your billowing sails
   gliding out on the seas of the morning
with bright flags flying and the sailors crying
and the wild winds blowing and the wild seas flowing
   and above you the Bird of Dawning:

To France and Spain and the Spanish Main
   and the Isles of Australia turning
your golden bows as the gale allows
when the green wave slides along your sides
   and you lean as though you were yearning

For some far shore where there's no more
   cloud or sorrow or weeping:
you flaunt your great sails through the storms and the
   gales
and in the calm night ride on the bright
   stars as though you were sleeping:

Ships proud and splendid, it is never ended
   your voyage into the morning.
Though in storms and rains and wild hurricanes
you welter and wallow, you will still follow
   the beautiful Bird of Dawning.

'My Heart Is Broken,'
Cried the Owl

'My heart is broken,' cried the Owl
  and the Moon answered: 'No.
Mop up your tears with a towel
Let no broken-hearted fowl
Rend the night with hoot and howl.
Mop up your tears with a towel.
  I am ashamed of you.'

The Owl repeated: 'Too whit too whoo'
  up at the angry Moon.
'Too whit too whoo, too whit too whoo.
It is all very well for you
Sitting up in the starry sky
With the Lion and Seven Sisters by,
But down here in the haunted tree
There is no one else but me.
I can feel my poor heart groan
Because –' he sobbed – 'I'm so alone.'
The Owl wept in his bitter grief
And wiped his eye upon a leaf.

'Come, Owl. Come, Owl,' the Moon replied.
  'It's not as bad as that.
Lift up your head and you will find
Stars all around you and your kind.
No Owl should ever quite despair
As long as I shine in the air.
Come, here's a slightly drier towel.
Cry Cheerio Cheerio, you old Owl.'

Tom Cat Tom Cat

Tom Cat Tom Cat
what are you at?
and why do you always behave
as though you had just
walked a long way in dust
to visit your grandmother's grave?

Tom Cat Tom Cat
when youngish you sat
by the fireside dreaming of nice
old ladies in mittens
who loved little kittens
and you never thought much about mice.

Tom Cat Tom Cat
the answer is that
as you get old but not better, a
fiendish delight
overcomes you at night
for hunting and stalking et cetera.

Tom Cat Tom Cat
I remember how fat
and full by the fire you slumbered
years ago, years ago
when the mouse did not know
as now, that its brief days are numbered.

Tom Cat Tom Cat
the mouse and the rat
at the pitter and pat
of your paw on the floor
like a large tiger paw
cross their hands on their breasts
in their shivering nests
and sigh with a fatal fore-knowledge:
'Is it us he is warning
this particular morning
he intends to dispatch with his porridge?'

The Death of a Cat

No, it was nothing much. Just the ginger
cat lying poisoned among ancient rusting
farm machinery in the stable, his pale blue
and gentle eyes filmed over and disgusting.

I cannot suppose his death has been recorded
in the heavenly archives but here in this
old house it certainly has been, simply because
if possession's nine points of the law, well, it was his.

Yes, this old farmhouse truly belonged to him: when,
six years ago a family came to this place
on a day of tumultuous rain and exhausted children
    and cold
winds as hostile as a spit in the face,

then, when, expecting little, we opened the door,
sitting up there in the hall, as small as a mouse,
this ginger kitten looked at us, turned, and then
led us like a walking welcome into the house.

A couple of years ago he was caught up
in a wire gin trap for a fortnight and more.
He lost a back leg. So he hunted on three.
(I hope he does so somewhere else on four.)

No, it is nothing much. The ginger cat
is dead, and buried. But then again, I see
those beautiful eyes occluded with a poison that
one day, my friend, may infect you, and me.

The Cheetah, My Dearest,
Is Known Not to Cheat

The cheetah, my dearest, is known not to cheat;
the Tiger possesses no tie;
The horse-fly, of course, was never a horse;
the lion will not tell a lie.

The turkey, though perky, was never a Turk;
nor the monkey ever a monk;
the mandrel, though like one, was never a man,
but some men are like him, when drunk.

The springbok, dear thing, was not born in the Spring;
The walrus will not build a wall.
No badger is bad; no adder can add.
There is no truth in these things at all.

January Jumps About

January jumps about
in the frying pan
trying to heat
his frozen feet
like a Canadian.

February scuttles under
any dish's lid
and she thinks she's dry because she's
thoroughly well hid
but it still rains all month long
and it always did.

March sits in the bath tub
with the taps turned on.
Hot and cold, cold or not,
Has the Winter gone?
In like a lion, out like a lamb
March on, march on, march on.

April slips about
sometimes indoors
and sometimes out
sometimes sheltering from a little
shower of bright rain
in an empty milk bottle
then dashing out again.

May, she hides nowhere,
nowhere at all,
Proud as a peacock
walking by a wall.
The Maytime O the Maytime
full of leaf and flower
The Maytime O the Maytime
is loveliest of all.

June discards his shirt and
trousers by the stream
and takes the first dip of the year
into a jug of cream.
June is the gay time
of every girl and boy
who run about and sing and shout
in pardonable joy.

July by the sea
sits dabbling with sand
letting it run out of
her rather lazy hand,
and sometimes she sadly
thinks: 'As I sit here
ah, more than half the year is gone,
the evanescent year.'

August by an emperor
was given his great name.
It is gold and purple
like a Hall of Fame.
(I have known it rather cold
and wettish, all the same.)

September lies in shadows
of the fading summer
hearing, in the distance,
the silver horns of winter
and not very far off
the coming autumn drummer.

October, October
apples on the tree,
the Partridge in the Wood and
the big winds at sea,
the mud beginning in the lane
the berries bright and red
and the big tree wildly
tossing its old head

November when the fires
love to burn, and leaves
flit about and fill the air
where the old tree grieves.
November, November
its name is like a star
glittering on many things that were
but few things that are.

Twelfth and last December.
A few weeks away
we hear the silver bells
of the stag and the sleigh
flying from the tundras
far far away
bringing to us all the gift
of our Christmas Day.

'The Great Gales Rage in the Trees'

The great gales rage in the trees outside the window.
   The moon races
over mottled water meadows and in shadows
   and moonlight the surfaces
   of the nightmare stream glint
and shiver in the wind as winter
   shrieks in the chimney stack
and not even the far obedient star
   believes it can ever bring
   the summer back.
The dog whimpers. A door slams. The shutters
   clap and a sleeping child
   stirs with a haunted sigh
   as the storm mutters
and groans around this dreaming and lonely
   house. From tossing trees
   the torn boughs
hang swaying dislocated, and uneasily
   the wood fire gutters
   as hisses and spits
   of rain sputter and drip
   into tiny blazes. I watch
   the year turning
   and burning to ash
   once more, once more
and hear the breathtaking grave-haunting wolf
   of death at the door.

from *Dreams of a Summer Night*

The shades of childhood
Rise before me
Turning away their
Forgotten faces
But still I see
Like a glass of tears
The eyes of childhood
Gaze upon me.

Why do they turn
Away from me
Every wild one of
My shades of childhood?
Each seems to see
The ghost of its conscience
Like a white presence
Standing by me.

Then who tell me who
Ah who are they
The forgotten faces
Mopping and mowing
In Time like a tree?
Foretelling foreknowing
All the sad stories
That are now the memories
Of what had to be.

Is it I or you
O shades of childhood
I hear mourning in
Time like a tree?
O angel shades
Rise up and cover
Our eyes so that we
Cannot see.

Never no never
Ever return to
That wild wood
Where like larks
We once rose and sang
O shades of childhood
Crowd now around me
As here in my heart our
Shadows hang.

I hear them sighing
Like voices that fade
When the song is over
As shade after shade
Falls away from me:
O shades of childhood
Farewell for ever.
Remember me. O
Remember me!

ALAN BROWNJOHN

Alan Brownjohn was born in Catford, south east London, in 1931, and educated at Brownhill Road Junior Mixed School, Brockley County School and Merton College, Oxford. He was a teacher and lecturer from 1953 to 1979 in a variety of schools (junior, secondary, comprehensive and boys' grammar) and was also involved in teacher training (Battersea College of Education and South Bank Polytechnic). He has been a freelance writer since 1979.

His books of poems include *The Railings* (Digby Press, 1961), *The Lions' Mouths* (Macmillan, 1967), *Sandgrains on a Tray* (Macmillan, 1969), *Warrior's Career* (Macmillan, 1972), *A Song of Good Life* (Secker and Warburg, 1975), *A Night in the Gazebo* (Secker & Warburg, 1980), *Collected Poems* (Secker & Warburg, 1983), and *The Old Flea-Pit* (Century Hutchinson, 1987). The *Collected Poems* have been reissued in paperback by Century Hutchinson. Some of the animal poems in this selection were in *Brownjohn's Beasts* (Macmillan, 1970). Alan Brownjohn's poems also appeared in a Penguin Modern Poets volume in 1969.

He has been poetry critic for two magazines, the *New Statesman* (1968–76) and *Encounter* (1977–80), and has written reviews of poetry, fiction and other books for *The Times Literary Supplement* for over twenty years. He is a frequent contributor to BBC poetry programmes, and has done many programmes for BBC School Radio. He has edited with his wife, Sandy Brownjohn, three teaching anthologies for schools called *Meet and Write*. Also with Sandy Brownjohn, he translated Goethe's play *Torquato Tasso* (broadcast on Radio 3 and published by Angel Books in 1985). In 1979 he received a Cholmondeley Award for poetry, and in 1985 was awarded a Travelling Scholarship from the Society of Authors.

40

I had already known Alan Brownjohn for some years, as our mutual interest in the reading and writing of poetry had led us to various events at the Poetry Society in Earls Court, London, where he is the chairman.

Alan was at infant school when he first became aware of poetry. The actual poem which started him off was Walter de la Mare's 'Silver', and the word-picture he most vividly remembers was the one about the dog in the moonlight:

> Crouched in his kennel like a log
> With paws of silver sleeps the dog.

He tried to write poetry when he was about six or seven, but his first real poems came later in his third year at secondary school. They were written in an exercise book and kept secret from everyone. I'm always fascinated to see poets' early writing, but he no longer has that secret book. All that remain are just a few poems from when he was fifteen; he didn't show them to me. Luckily, he has kept some volumes of his diary written around the same time.

Alan is a city man with five generations of Londoners on one side of his family, three on the other. He grew up in south London and went to school there, apart from his time as an evacuee in the Second World War. Like me he spent part of the war in Cornwall, and perhaps also like me, time away from town life gave him a feeling for the country. Certainly nowadays he divides his time between a flat in Hampstead, north London, and a small house in Norfolk. He likes the change of place, and enjoys writing in different settings.

It was his flat that I visited, a comfortable, homely place with a lived-in feeling. As always, my eyes were drawn straight to the bookshelves and especially to an enviable collection of over 2,000 poetry books. I asked him about his hobbies, and he said he had 'interests' rather than 'hobbies' and no longer collected anything like stamps or matchboxes. His interests are wide and include all aspects of world affairs, classical music of all periods, modern jazz and films. He is a passionate admirer of Shakespeare and is always fascinated to see Shakespeare plays in other languages and countries. *Macbeth* in Japanese (in London), *Hamlet* in Finnish (in Helsinki), *As You Like It* in Romanian (in Bucharest).

The poems I've chosen come from Alan's adult writing as well as his children's collection *Brownjohn's Beasts*, which he wrote for his son, Steven. We agreed that children don't always need poems specially written for them, and that many adult choices are well within their grasp. We agreed, too, on the importance of the teacher's enthusiasm in the poetry lesson. Alan himself taught for many years and now he is a freelance writer, still takes poetry workshops, mainly for the Arvon Foundation in Devon and Yorkshire. With his wife, Sandy, he has published three anthologies called *Meet and Write*. Sandy Brownjohn is well known for her books on writing poetry, entitled *Does It Have to Rhyme?* and *What Rhymes With Secret?*

Real happenings, real fears, mysteries, all these are in his poems. Finding a war badge in the bushes, recalling a teacher's saying – small moments are recaptured. Sometimes, as in 'Crabwise', facts make up the substance of the poem. In 'Grey Ground' a rather unreal fear of treading on some safe, ordinary ground as a child, returns as a genuine adult fear. 'Going to See the Rabbit' is his most popularly anthologized poem, and makes a firm and bitter comment on progress.

When you meet Alan you are aware of a kind, gentle man with a lovely sense of humour. He is extremely popular with other poets as a friend and colleague. The off-beat direction his poems can take, the underlying darkness, the touches of surrealism, might come as a shock. From the beginning he found his poems needed to be redrafted several times, and there can be about twenty versions of a poem before he feels satisfied with the result. It is important for him to write well on the ideas he cares about.

I wondered whether he subtitled 'Chant' a homage to Walter de la Mare, because of the early impression made on him by 'Silver'. In it he writes 'I call my cat Rover' . . .

Just as I was leaving a beautiful Manx cat padded out from behind some furniture . . . not called Rover at all. Her name is Thisbe.

Chant

(Homage to Walter de la Mare)

I call my cat Rover
Sound the bell
Sound the bell five times over

His paws will feel before me in the night
Ring the bell right
Sound the bell five times over

His paws will feel before me in the night
His blue eyes will shine the forest walk
Let the bell talk
Sound the bell five times over

His paws will feel before me in the night
His blue eyes will shine the forest walk
His nose will sniff the key in the tree-hole
Make the notes toll
Sound the bell five times over

I call my cat Rover

His paws will feel before me in the night
His blue eyes will shine the forest walk
His nose will sniff the key in the tree-hole
His tongue will know by taste the courtyard air
Clang bell and send us to the stair
Sound the bell five times over

His paws will feel before me in the night
His blue eyes will shine the forest walk
His nose will sniff the key in the tree-hole
His tongue will know by taste the courtyard air
His ears will flick at any footfall
Have the bell swing and call
Sound the bell five times over

Rover knows the dark the path and the secret tree
Knows the castle keep and the spiral stair
Knows the box and the twisted key

I call my cat Rover

Explorer

Two o'clock:
Let out of the back door of the house, our cat
Is practising the snow.

The layer of white makes a small, straight, crumbling
    cliff
Where we open the back door inwards. The cat
Sniffs it with suspicion, learns you can just about
Pat the flaking snow with a careful dab. Then,
A little bolder, he dints it with one whole foot
– and withdraws it, curls it as if slightly lame,

And looks down at it, oddly. The snow is
Different from anything else, not like
A rug, or a stretch of lino, or an armchair to claw
    upon
And be told to *Get off!*

The snow is peculiar, but not forbidden. The cat
Is welcome to go out in the snow. Does
The snow welcome the cat?
He thinks, looks, tries again.

Three paces out of the door, his white feet find
You sink a little way all the time, it is slow and cold,
    but it
Doesn't particularly hurt. Perhaps you can even enjoy
    it, as something new.
So he walks on, precisely, on the tips of very cautious
    paws . . .

Half-past three, the cat stretched warm indoors,
From the bedroom window we can see his explora-
   tions

– From door to fence, from fence to gate, from gate to
   wall to tree, and back,
Are long pattered tracks and trade-routes of round
   paw-marks
Which fresh snow is quietly filling.

Cat

Sometimes I am an unseen
marmalade cat, the friendliest colour,
making off through a window without permission,
pacing along a broken-glass wall to the
   greenhouse
jumping down with a soft, four-pawed thump,
finding two inches open of the creaking door
with the loose brass handle,
slipping impossibly in,
flattening my fur at the hush and touch of
   the sudden warm air,
avoiding the tiled gutter of slow green water,
skirting the potted nests of tetchy cactuses,
and sitting with my tail flicked
skilfully underneath me, to sniff
the azaleas   the azaleas   the azaleas.

Dog

What could a terrier better be
than trimmed all thin for the summer,
half my winter size,
lean and eager with
smiling, wire-haired energy for
altogether everything.
                    Stop me
– the sun is shining – from all this
bouncing about indoors among
groups of aunts in chairs,
stop me offering myself with
lapping tongue to silent postmen,
stop me knocking over peonies in vases.
                            Take me
to a lot of cropped grass and hurl me
on four scratching legs
after a bitten rubber ball
into the middle distance.

Ant

I am
a persistent ant climbing a
tall brown table-leg

up to the fawn hem of
a curtain completely covered
in vermilion poppies and

little mauve moons. In
three seconds, I'll
be among the colours

creeping enjoyably,
thinking how other
ants might like this

– any colour-loving ant.

Crabwise

Sea-crabs live in
And near the sea,
Land-crabs go back
Occasionally.

After these many months the old crab was out of the
     water,
And into the full, blank air and wanting the sun.

A crab has a very strange
Sideways walk
And eyes placed on
A retracting stalk.

Wide sheets of wet light covered the level beach
As he came fumbling and peering over the gnarled sand.

Two kinds of bodies
For crabs there are:
The oval and
The triangular.

His ten legs carried his squat bulk grave-
ly and slowly like a burden altogether too sad to keep
     long.

A little crab only
Really begins
To be adult when he's
Cast five skins.

This was his last stroll of years out of the bitter flow
   and
Hard swirl of the winter water, dragging from pool to
   clear pool.

        A crab's feet are not
        All the same, because
        Some are for walking
        And some have jaws.

His old mouths muttered on the windy silence as he
   walked.
In his funny clumsiness and misery he was man-like.

Whale

I am a whale and
seven hundred miles off Valparaiso the
horizon has been an empty circle for six
hundred and fifty miles.

There is nothing on the moving
earth like this moving sea where I wallow,
master,
where I swallow acres of water daily, where I
spout high fountains of water, hourly.

Land wouldn't
contain me, I would have to contain *it*:
whole towns and mountains, whole
assemblies of arguing governments, whole
countries, whole continents.

I think sometimes
I could take in the whole globe itself and
swim like water the sad air in which
it turns around the sun

(at least, when I am boasting
it *feels* like this).

Elephant

It is quite unfair to be
obliged to be so large, so I suppose
you could call me discontented.

Think big, they said, when
I was a little elephant; they
wanted to get me used to it.

It was kind. But it doesn't help if,
inside, you are carefree in small ways,
fond of little amusements.

You are smaller than me, think
how conveniently near the flowers are,
how you can pat the cat by just

half bending over. You can also
arrange teacups for dolls, play
marbles in the proper season.

I would give anything to be
able to do a tiny, airy, flitting
dance to show how very little a

thing happiness can be really.

In Daylight Strange

It was last Friday at ten to four I
Thought of the lion walking into the playground.
I was sitting, thinking, at our table when
The thought of the lion simply came,
And the sun was very hot, and the lion
Was in the yard (in daylight strange, because
Lions go out at night). He was
An enormous, sudden lion and he
Appeared just like that and was crossing very
Slowly the dusty playground, looking
To neither side, coming towards the door. He was
Coloured a yellow that was nearly grey, or a
Grey that was nearly yellow. He was so
Quiet that only I could hear the huge feet
Solidly pacing, and at the playground door he
Stopped, and looked powerfully in. There was
A forest following him, out in the street,
And noises of parakeets. When he stopped,
Looking like a picture of a lion in the frame
Of the open door, his eyes looked on at
Everything inside with a stern, curious look, he
Didn't seem completely to understand. So
He waited a second or two before
He roared. All the reeds on the river bank
Trembled, a thousand feet
Scattered among the trees, birds rose in clouds
But no one jumped in the classroom, no one screamed,
No one ran to ring the firebell, and
Miss Wolfenden went on writing on the board.
It was just exactly as if

They hadn't heard at all, as if nobody had heard.
And yet I had heard, certainly,
Yes. I had heard,
And I didn't jump.
And would you say you were surprised? Because
You ought not to be surprised.
Why should I be frightened when it was
Because *I* thought of the lion, that the lion was there?

Inheritors

The snow is at the same time as the owl;
When it drops down to the sill, the wings close,

First question: *Why should the owl*
Fly down each night to peer at our painted room?

Softly the snow-dots tumble from its back
As it stands on still claws and looks in,

Second question: *Why does the owl*
Stare in so long at our wine and velvet chairs?

Away from its nest, old feathers, suspicious gaze,
Away if you walk near the window, but always back,

Third question: *If one of us has summoned it,*
Which?

– And so we sit, four men in a shared house,
In a particularly scarlet room,
Not easy as we snow down cards, four
After four on the shining table-top;

Not easy as our fingers claw them in;
Wondering what is meant by these visits
From two old interested eyes, not easy
Wondering also which of us might know.

Heptonstall February

Today the moors unclench and clench
On a gift of warmth, the snow
Draws back one softened inch, but frost holds firm.
In our mid-afternoon new ice already
Glints in the sun's very eye. A camera eye
Would trace the loosened stream, and stop
On a rigid freeze: where suddenly grey
Spires, that were a waterfall, stab down
At the shrunken torrent.
                              None of these days
Will release themselves, the land
Not gentle into sympathy. This cold
Is well ignored by those who wait indoors
Inside their coloured windows, watching
The month increase and the land not change:
Let it come to the light and listen.

Grey Ground

In the Cornwall wind
I stood with the mine-shaft behind me.
Something said, a toneless kind-of-voice said, 'Don't
Walk on that ground.'

The ground was plain mud and stones, a grey stretch,
    safe.
But, 'Don't walk on that ground.'
I had flung and heard the pebbles in the dark shaft
Fenced off under the brick stack, black.
Was the grey ground not safe?

The wind worked at the firs' tops,
It had that whisper, 'Don't walk on
That ground.' The pebbles in the shaft
Clanged, and hit echoes. The echoes touched out
Echoes. The echoes said, 'Don't walk on that
Ground.'

The death-shaft gulped and trapped the echoes of the
    pebbles.
The ground was mud and stones, is mud and stones,
A grey stretch, not fenced off now, thirty years
Safe, still. People have walked on it,
Thirty years.
I did not walk on it when I was ten.

I stand here, thirty years after, in the Cornwall wind
A man, looking at the grey ground. The firs' tops
Work and whisper.
The day is a clearer day, the sea visible,

The sun is out. A woman touches my arm,
We are standing with the mine-shaft behind us
    swallowing
Echoes of thirty years ago, of a minute ago,
Pebbles we have both thrown, smiling.

Something says, a toneless kind-of-voice says
'Don't walk on that ground.'

Before the Game

This is the coin
spinning in air
to decide who wins the toss.

This is the thumb that flicked the coin
spinning in air
to decide who wins the toss.

This is the hand that owns the thumb
that flicked the coin
spinning in air
to decide who wins the toss.

This is the brain that controls the hand
that owns the thumb
that flicked the coin
spinning the air
to decide who wins the toss.

And this, over here, is the twelfth man,
who lent the coin
as a method of being noticed for something,
if not for his part in the game.

It is the custom here that the loser of the toss
keeps the coin as a consolation
for the brutality of Fate.

The owner of this coin did not know of the custom,
or he would not have lent for the purpose
a rare doubloon
of the Emperor Paronomasia IV.

As it spins he watches it, trying to seem unaffected,
thinking, 'Will I ever get it back?'

The situation is complicated by the fact
that the doubloons of the Emperor Paronomasia IV
have two heads.

Fire Drill

Now we all troop out, now we all troop out
Along the arrows on the notices;

But it's not for real, they told us in advance
There was going to be an exercise.

The hooter blares on down long corridors
And over into portakabins. Here

Is a word half-finished on a typewriter,
There, a comb stopped in half-done hair. Miss West,

Never seen full-length before, is standing up
And out from behind her desk, Mr Vince

Hasn't rescued the word-processor from the flames,
But he has saved some important-looking memos.

What would we do, we say, if it were true,
And not a practice! Leaving our coats inside,

We pour out, as instructed, from the main doors
And the side doors; and all protocol has gone.

On the equal grass today's warm sun and breeze
Flow round our unusual outdoor laughter,

And anyone talks to anyone. Back inside,
In the empty spaces, nothing can be the same.

We shall go back with a sense of changing,
To rooms where the sun falls in a different place.

– But we can't go back, they want a photograph.
They want a photograph and had not told us.

Stand still – like that – stand still, *stand still*!
There is going to be a tremendous flash.

Of All the Eccentrics

Mr Croker was the oddest,
Living in a Yorkshire cottage
With his Nicaraguan terrier
And his pair of Swedish bagpipes.
Every time he sent his laundry,
He would put a poem in it
Written out in neat handwriting,
Written for the laundry ladies
Who would open up his parcels
(Full of most peculiar laundry)
And would come upon the poem
Wrapped up in a sheet or towel
And would shout to one another
'Ah, this must be Mr Croker's!
What do you think he's sent us *this* time?'
Standing round their big machines where
Dirty laundry churned and tangled,
They would drop their washing powder,
Cluster round and read the poems,
Which were sometimes turgid epics
Written out on greaseproof paper,
Or they could be dainty verses,
Rhymed, with violets in the margins,
Or they might be crazy offerings
with no
       sense or
             rhyme or
                   meter
written without capital lett-
                      ers

lacking any punctuation
Every week he sent his laundry
Punctually on Friday mornings,
Every week the laundry workers
Opened it and read the poems,
Pinned them on the wall and learnt them
(All those not too mad or boring),
Sang them, as they did the washing,
To the tunes on their transistors,
Till the laundry walls were covered
And there was nowhere to put them.

Then he sent another poem.
That was one fine day in April,
One cold sunny day in April
(Everything was bright and windy)
When the heartiest laundry lady
Didn't really feel like working
And the big machines were stacked with
Much more stuff than they could handle,
And the poem that he sent them,
Rather odd but very lively,
Was especially gay and cheerful,
Full of spring and life and dancing.

Standing on a pile of washing,
One fat, humorous laundry lady
Read the poem to the others
And then said, 'I'm tired of toiling.
Let's all leave and go and see him,
Him that wrote us all these poems.
I don't want to work this morning,
Which of you is coming with me

Up to Mr Croker's cottage?
Shall we take a vote upon it?'
But there was so loud a chorus,
All the laundry ladies shouting,
'Let's leave work and go and see him!'
That there was no time for voting.

In a sturdy, laughing, singing,
Dancing line they left the laundry,
Down the street and past the junction
Up the hill and round the corner,
Up the One Way quite the wrong way
In the middle of the roadway,
Halting all the morning traffic,
Aggravating all the policemen,
Till they saw the purple curtains

In the grimy cottage windows
Where they stopped. And in a circle,
Stood round Mr Croker's cottage
Singing, 'It's a fabulous morning,
Mr Croker, come and join us!'
Then, at one dim upstairs window,
Mr Croker's face appearing
(He was wearing his pyjamas
Till they sent him back his laundry)
Made them sing out all the louder,
'Mr Croker, please don't scold us,
We don't feel like washing socks and
Pants and vests and towels and trousers,
(Thanks for sending us the poems),
We would rather go out dancing
Up the hill to MacBeth's meadow.
Won't you, *won't* you come and join us,
We shall not be moved!'
                              Whereupon,
Mr Croker, slowly smiling,
Called out, 'Wait a moment, wait a
Moment, I'll come down and join you,
Wait until I've fetched my bagpipes,
Found the lead and woken Walrus'
– Odd name for a Nicaraguan
Terrier – 'and we'll go out dancing
If you won't mind my pyjamas.'

Up the hill, with Mr Croker
Leading (being led by Walrus)
Danced three dozen laundry ladies
Singing Mr Croker's poems
To the tunes on their transistors,

Till they came to MacBeth's meadow
Which was on a sunny hilltop.
There they sang and danced all day – till
In the windy April evening
One small shower fell down around them,
And they stopped and wandered homeward –
Looking from the distance like a
Row of washing out for drying,
And the nasty laundry foreman
Couldn't stop them, and was furious.
That week we all got our laundry
One day late. But no one grumbled.

1939

Where the ball ran into the bushes,
And I was sent to find it, being
Useful for that more than to play their game,
I saw instead
This badge, from someone's brother, in
Some regiment of that war: a trophy
Begged for and polished, coveted certainly,
But lost now, slightly touched with dust already,
Yet shining still, under smooth leaves drab with dust.
I knew that people prized such trophies then,
It was the way of all of us. I might,
For no one looked, have taken it
For mine. I valued it. It shone
For me as much as anyone.
And yet some fear or honesty, some sense
It wasn't to be mine – it wasn't more –
Said No to all of this. Besides,
They shouted in the distance for their ball.
For once quite quickly, I
Made up my mind
And left the thing behind.

Marginalia

When it was Munich, I was eight.
Miss Adams made her point like this:
'Without a ruler, no one can
Draw me a line that's truly straight.'
And thus, to make her meaning plain:
'Not even any famous man:
Herr Hitler. Mr Chamberlain.'

And through the years, one might infer,
Miss Adams used such other names
As fitted best the days she came
To teach this truth, beloved of her:
'Not even Mr Stalin, and
Sir Winston Churchill, he's the same,
Could draw me one straight line freehand.'

And I should think that through that door,
In one of those brown passages,
I might still find her echoing room
Somewhere along the lower floor;
And hear again that doctrine taught,
To forty different minds for whom
It would seem just as strange a thought.

'No one who thinks that he can draw
Straight lines without a ruler, will
Ever surprise me if he fails –
What do you think your ruler's *for*?
There isn't anyone at all
Could do it. Not the Prince of Wales!
Not even General de Gaulle!'

You'll See

They all talked about growing into,
Growing into, growing into.
They said: You will grow into it.

– But it isn't mine,
And it's not for me.
– You will grow into it,
You'll see!

– But it hangs down below my knee,
It is too long for me.
– Oh it will fit you soon,
It will fit you splendidly.

– But I will sulk, and I will say
It is too long, it is no use,
No! I will sulk, and struggle,
And refuse!

– You will grow into it,
And love it,
And besides, we decided
You should have it.

No! – But wait –
Wait a moment . . . Do I see
It growing shorter at the knee?
Is it shrinking gradually?
Is it getting shorter?
Is it getting tighter?

Not loose and straggly,
Not long and baggy,
But neater and brighter,
Comfortable?

Oh now I *do* like it,
Oh now I'll go to the mirror and see
How wonderful it looks on me,
Yes – there – it's ideal!
Yes, its appeal
Will be universal,
And now I curse all
Those impulses which muttered 'Refuse!'
It's really beautiful after all,
I'll wear it today, next week, next year
– No one is going to interfere,
I'll wear it as long as I choose.

And then, much later, when it wears,
And it's ready for dumping under the stairs
When it doesn't actually really fit me
Any longer, then *I'll* pass it down,
When it doesn't fit me,
And then they'll have it,
They'll *have* to have it,
They'll have to love it,
They'll see, they'll see.

They'll have to grow into it like me!

Common Sense

An agricultural labourer, who has
A wife and four children, receives 20s a week.
¾ buys food, and the members of the family
Have three meals a day.
How much is that per person per meal?
– *From Pitman's Common Sense Arithmetic, 1917*

A gardener, paid 24s a week, is
Fined 1/3 if he comes to work late.
At the end of 26 weeks, he receives
£30.5.3. How
Often was he late?
– *From Pitman's Common Sense Arithmetic, 1917*

A milk dealer buys milk at 3d a quart. He
Dilutes it with 3% water and sells
124 gallons of the mixture at
4d per quart. How much of his profit is made by
Adulterating the milk?
– *From Pitman's Common Sense Arithmetic, 1917*

The table printed below gives the number
Of paupers in the United Kingdom, and
The total cost of poor relief.
Find the average number
Of paupers per ten thousand people.
– *From Pitman's Common Sense Arithmetic, 1917*

An army had to march to the relief of
A besieged town, 500 miles away, which

74

Had telegraphed that it could hold out for 18 days.
The army made forced marches at the rate of 18
Miles a day. Would it be there in time?
– *From Pitman's Common Sense Arithmetic, 1917*

Out of an army of 28,000 men,
15% were
Killed, 25% were
Wounded. Calculate
How many men there were left to fight.
– *From Pitman's Common Sense Arithmetic, 1917*

These sums are offered to
That host of young people in our Elementary Schools,
     who
Are so ardently desirous of setting
Foot upon the first rung of the
Educational ladder . . .
– *From Pitman's Common Sense Arithmetic, 1917*

'We Are Going to See the Rabbit . . .'

We are going to see the rabbit,
We are going to see the rabbit.
Which rabbit, people say?
Which rabbit, ask the children?
Which rabbit?
The only rabbit,
The only rabbit in England,
Sitting behind a barbed-wire fence
Under the floodlights, neon lights,
Sodium lights,
Nibbling grass
On the only patch of grass
In England, in England
(Except the grass by the hoardings
Which doesn't count.)
We are going to see the rabbit
And we must be there on time.

First we shall go by escalator,
Then we shall go by underground,
And then we shall go by motorway
And then by helicopterway,
And the last ten yards we shall have to go
On foot.

And now we are going
All the way to see the rabbit.
We are nearly there,
We are longing to see it,
And so is the crowd

Which is here in thousands
With mounted policemen
And big loudspeakers
And bands and banners,
And everyone has come a long way.
But soon we shall see it
Sitting and nibbling
The blades of grass
On the only patch of grass
In – but something has gone wrong!
Why is everyone so angry,
Why is everyone jostling
And slanging and complaining?

The rabbit has gone,
Yes, the rabbit has gone.
He has actually burrowed down into the earth
And made himself a warren, under the earth,
Despite all these people.
And what shall we do?
What *can* we do?

It is all a pity, you must be disappointed,
Go home and do something else for today,
Go home again, go home for today.
For you cannot hear the rabbit, under the earth,
Remarking rather sadly to himself, by himself,
As he rests in his warren, under the earth:
'It won't be long, they are bound to come,
They are bound to come and find me, even here.'

Parrot

Sometimes I sit with both eyes closed,
But all the same, I've heard!
They're saying, 'He won't talk because
He is a *thinking* bird.'

I'm olive-green and sulky, and
The family say, 'Oh yes,
He's silent, but he's *listening*,
He *thinks* more than he *says*!

'He ponders on the things he hears,
Preferring not to chatter.'
– And this is true, but *why* it's true
Is quite another matter.

I'm working out some shocking things
In order to surprise them,
And when my thoughts are ready I'll
Certainly *not* disguise them!

I'll wait, and see, and choose a time
When everyone is present,
And clear my throat and raise my beak
And give a squawk and start to speak
And go on for about a week
And it will not be pleasant!

Pigeon

Standing on an old chimney-pot in a
smokeless zone on a warm and quite
cloudless morning in late June,
turning my head from time to time
to pick at some itchy feather or other,
doing nothing except watch the world taking
    place,
I think:
       it took me a long time to be good at this,
it needed months of practice and careful
    thought
and I don't think those seagulls who only
come here because a mere stormy sea is
too much for them
can hope to do this with anything like my skill.

How You Move House

Your Mum or Dad brings a huge box
For packing everything that's small,
And stuff that rattles: plates, and crocks,
And ornaments from off the wall,

And things you wrap in cloths because
They'd break, and vases from the shelves,
And oddments from the sideboard drawers
– And this you do all by yourselves,

But one March morning, three or four
Removal men come with their van,
And set to work to load all your
Big beds and tables (one strong man

Carries the fridge out on his own)
And suddenly there's nothing there!
Each room seems just as if it's grown
To twice its size. The house *sounds* bare.

They dump the large things deep inside
The lorry first, and then they take
Your box, and heave it up beside
The rest, and still they need to make

Space for your curtains, clothes and books,
While back indoors you notice that
It's not your home, the whole place looks
Too light . . . And then you seize the cat,

And drive off to the new house, where
They've worked so fast, you can't remember
These rooms of furniture were bare
When you first called here, in December.

And when you wander round and see
The things you brought, they all appear
A little strange. Those chairs must be
The same chairs; but they're *different* here . . .

Skipping Rhyme

Páin óf the leáf, ońe twó –
Wórd óf the stóne, thŕee, fóur –
Fóot óf the dárk, pít óf the hánd,
Heárt óf the cloúd, fíve, síx, ańd
Oút!
   Sḱip.
Nóra sh́e had wh́ite eýes,
Máry sh́e had bláck –́
Helen looḱed in Gréy Man's Woód and
Néver cańe
Back!
   Juḿp.
Nóra dráws a gréen threád,
Máry spińs it blúe –́
But Helen wíll not bińd it tíll her
Trúe Lóve mákes it
Trúe!
   Quíck!
Ońe, twó, leáf of the páin,
Thŕee, fóur, stóne of the wórd,
Fíve, síx, dárk of the fóot, hánd of the pít,
Clóud of the heárt, ańd
OÚT!

LEONARD CLARK

Leonard Clark was born in St Peter Port, Guernsey, on 1 August 1905. He was educated at Monmouth School and the Normal College, Bangor, Caernarthonshire, and received the Certificate of Education in 1930. He served in the Devon Regiment of the Home Guard from 1940 to 1943. He married Jane Callow in 1954 and they had two children. He taught in Gloucestershire and London from 1930 to 1936, and from 1936 to 1970 was an Inspector of Schools. From 1970 he was the Editor of Longman's Poetry Library series (sixty-four titles), and was a member of the Arts Council Literature Panel from 1965 to 1969. In 1965 he was made a Freeman of the City of London. He was a Fellow of the Royal Society of Literature in 1953, and a Knight of the Order of St Sylvester in 1970. In 1966 he received the OBE. He was General Editor of Chatto Poets for the Young from 1970 to 1978.

His published work includes *Passage to the Pole* (Fortune Press, 1944), *The Mirror* (Allan Wingate, 1948), *English Morning* (Hutchinson, 1953), *Daybreak* and *The Year Round* (Hart-Davis, 1964/5), *Good Company* and *Near and Far* (Dobson, 1968), *Here and There* (Hamlyn, 1969), *Walking with Trees* (Enitharmon, 1969), *Secret as Toads* (Chatto & Windus, 1974), *Singing in the Streets* (Dobson, 1972), *The Broad Atlantic* (Dobson, 1974), *The Hearing Heart* (Enitharmon, 1975), *Collected Poems for Children* (Dobson, 1975), *Stranger than Unicorns* (Dobson, 1979), *The Singing Time* (Hodder & Stoughton, 1980), *The Way it Was* (Enitharmon, 1980), *The Corn Growing* (Hodder & Stoughton, 1982). His anthologies include *Drums and Trumpets*, 1962 and *Flutes and Cymbals*, 1969 (both Bodley Head). His prose work includes *Sark Discovered* (Dent, 1956), *Walter de la Mare; a check list*

(Cambridge University Press, 1956), *Walter de la Mare: A Bodley Head Monograph* (1960), *Green Wood* (Parish, 1962), *Andrew Young* (Longman, 1964), *A Fool in the Forest* (Dobson, 1965), *Grateful Caliban* (Dobson, 1967), *The Inspector Remembers* (Dobson, 1975). Leonard Clark died in Highgate, London, in 1981.

Leonard Clark was brought up in a little mining town in the Forest of Dean, surrounded by trees, hills and fields and near the two rivers, Severn and Wye. His earliest memories were of wandering through the fields, discovering ancient cattle tracks and Roman roads, losing himself in the tangled growth of the trees. On a clear day he could see the tower of Gloucester Cathedral from a hilltop.

When he was small, the most exciting event was a visit to Gloucester with his mother in a horse-brake for a day's shopping, meeting friends and seeing the sights. They would start at 6.30 a.m. and 'there would be much polishing of boots, brushing down of clothes, packing of sandwiches, counting of pennies.' Sunday best was the rule and Leonard would wear 'white lace collar, Norfolk breeches and squeaking boots.' The brasses and lamps of Dan Walkley's brake gleamed in the early sun, and the horses clip-clopped through villages, past meadows, churches, streams and inns. Once, as they journeyed through acres of flowering fruit-trees, Leonard jumped up and shouted to the other silent passengers: 'Oh, look at those trees!'

It was his mother, Sarah, who taught him about the countryside. She was actually his foster-mother, though he doesn't say much about the circumstances of his birth in his autobiographies. He came to Sarah as a baby, inheriting three foster-brothers named Alan, Fred and William. They called the baby 'Bob'. He said: 'From Sarah ... I learned about gardens and birds and hedgerows ... it was she who encouraged me to use my eyes and ears and to wander freely along the country lanes and through the deep woods ... It was from Sarah's lips that I first heard the folk-songs of the long ago, and stories and poems on winter nights, and all about May Day, Midsummer and Hallowe'en. She had her own box of recipes and knew the weather signs and where to find the first wild strawberries.'

The headmaster of Leonard's country school was strict and eccentric, but taught his classes to love words and people. He worshipped Shakespeare and taught them about his works before they reached the age of eleven.

'Because you live in a forest,' he used to thunder, 'you are not wild animals. Therefore you must speak the King's English.'

Leonard was an observant boy and the sights and sounds of his country childhood never lost their magic. In his reminiscences he wrote about the first boxing match he ever watched, the first girl he liked, local concerts and flowers shows and the day that 'the fiercest lion in captivity' escaped from a travelling circus, trotted in to the vicar's parlour and lay down by the fire. Some incidents and characters he kept for his poems, like 'Charles', the blind organist in the local church who was 'all imagination when it came to accompanying the psalms. He gave to me the music of my childhood and the love of Handel's music in particular.' 'Dwarf' is also based on a real character.

Leonard began writing very early, and by the age of fifteen had poems published regularly in the local newspaper. At seventeen he got to know F. W. (Will) Harvey who lived close by and who is best known for his poem 'Ducks'. The two shared an enthusiasm for cricket and poetry, with Will encouraging the boy to read more widely, and introducing him to Chaucer and Thomas Hardy.

On leaving school he trained as a teacher, with ambitions to work towards a headship. Instead he became a school inspector, which entailed travelling all over the country and abroad. As he moved into a more senior position, he found opportunities to introduce ideas for poetry and literature to the Ministry of Education (later the Department of Education and Science). He had a major hand in establishing an annual poetry course and in persuading distinguished poets to give readings.

In *The Inspector Remembers* he says: 'The work I did in the field of poetry and especially poetry in education, has, perhaps, given me the greatest satisfaction and especially when I saw the establishment of the Arts Council's Writers in Schools scheme, for this was an idea dear to my heart.'

In an immensely busy and varied career, Leonard Clark collected many friends in all walks of life and published numerous books. Apart from his original writing, he showed excellent taste and a discerning eye in compiling anthologies and in editing the poets he most admired, notably Ivor Gurney, Andrew Young and Walter de la Mare. His association with de la Mare began at the age of nine when he read the poem 'Silver' (just as Alan Brownjohn did) in a copy of *Peacock Pie* he had begged Sarah to buy from a stall in Gloucester. He wrote to 'the man with the funny name', objecting to the use of 'shoon' as the plural of shoe to rhyme with 'moon'. In his courteous reply the famous poet urged the little boy to look in Chaucer and Webster's dictionary.

Thirty-four years later Leonard dedicated a book of poems, *The Mirror*, to de la Mare. The two became close friends. One day Leonard was invited to take his baby son, Robert, to visit the poet in Twickenham, and the child spent most of the time playing with a handbell on the bedside table. When Walter de la Mare died the bell was sent to Robert Clark, as you can read about in the final poem.

Leonard Clark died in 1981 but I was able to meet his son, Bob, who actually brought the famous bell to show me. Bob recalled how, a few weeks before Leonard died, they had talked over many things in depth, including the background to some of his poems. Through Bob I discovered that 'The Quilt' and 'The Button Box' both belonged to Sarah, that 'Glass' was a favourite poem of Leonard's, and that he reworked his poems over and over again until he felt satisfied.

Our talk gave me a more vivid picture of Leonard Clark: a small man (he was only five foot two), bespectacled, hardworking, enthusiastic, who had a strong influence on poetry for young people.

Early Portrait

A country boy,
exiled now in London, bred in Gloucestershire
where Severn flows serenely, the white cathedral
    tower,
a secure and Norman landmark beneath Cotswold
    skies.
Brought up among trees, Forest of Dean,
coal mines glimpsed over heads of foxgloves;
wandered, a dreamer, bluebelled glades all hours, day
    and night
knew where foxes hid, once saw a golden eagle;
sang with small but true voice in the church choir, no
    angel,
with corn-coloured curls could have been mistaken for
    one,
stocky, sharp-eyed, a fleet runner, eager to please,
very vulnerable, easily brought to tears;
played village cricket, did not excel,
outgoing by nature, knew many gypsies, tramps,
often in trouble, plagued my mother and teachers,
eyed girls nervously, too shy to approach one.
At Monmouth school, scholarship boy, but poor,
learned the Latin tongue, little French, no mathematics,
a rough and cunning rugby player;
an odd mixture, loved music, poetry,
all strange and rural things, the changing seasons,
had green fingers, an eager, bespectacled reader.

Knew sorrow, disappointment, never hunger,
had perfect health, not easily daunted,

stumbled along somehow, my chilhood days,
guided by some light glowing within me,
never lost a sense of wonder.

Aware now though of mistakes I made,
my hot temper and impatience,
grateful for good fortune, home and friends,
loyal to their memory, count my blessings,
looking calmly into the future,
a country boy still,
exiled now in London.

Small Birds

Quiet morning, the new year's first day
Written in words of frost upon the almanac;
Dark birds now flutter down, peck away
In circles round each littered barn and stack.
They gather there in busy, greedy throngs,
Eyes full of corn, not caring that it snows;
Sharp hunger puts an edge on all their songs.
The weather turns them into dominoes,
Changes the shape of every tree and shed
As one by one they feed, until the night
Begins to cancel out each toy-like, bobbing head,
And all their world is either black or white.

Daffodils

Bulbs planted, their long, cool sleep begins,
Laid away in the dark, three bowls,
Life locked-up, sunlight hidden in tight folds.
Two months, for winter's green blades
To pierce the chill air, welcome a new year.
Some morning of surprise a dozen trumpets will sound
The dark's ending with a gold salute.
The world will shine then, three bowls
Make the house beautiful with a little spring,
My eyes full of flowers.

In March

At winter's end when hungry foxes sleep
A few uneasy hours in earthy dens,
And shivering hares squat in their forms, and sheep
At lambing time bed down in farmyard pens;
Then stiff with cold in secret garden holes
Thin dormice lie, curled up with drowsy moles.

Before the frosty darkness falls outside,
There flit on faintly coloured wing a pair
Of chaffinches who on the branches hide,
For they have found a quiet lodging where
They, too, can settle down this night and rest,
And in the morning start to build their nest.

And in the farmhouse now our yawning cat,
After a busy day begins to tire,
And lies there warm and sleek and fat,
Stretched out beside the blazing kitchen fire;
Dreaming and purring she is well away,
It is the ending of a chill March day.

So wild and tame have skies above their heads
Where all the stars of early springtime shine.
They go contented to their peaceful beds,
And I am full of sleep and go to mine.

First Primrose

I saw it in the lane
One morning going to school
After a soaking night of rain,
The year's first primrose,
Lying there familiar and cool
In its private place
Where little else grows
Beneath dripping hedgerows,
Stalk still wet, face
Pale as Inca gold,
Spring glistening in every delicate fold.
I knelt down by the roadside there,
Caught the faint whiff of its shy scent
On the cold and public air,
Then got up and went
On my slow way,
Glad and grateful I'd seen
The first primrose that day,
Half yellow, half green.

Midsummer Night

Down by the river I heard a voice crying
Over the waters with never a word,
O, was it the wind in the willow trees sighing,
Or the sound of a bird?

Into the forest I saw a shape glancing,
When the creatures had settled down safe for the night,
O, was it the moon on the mossy banks dancing,
Or a trick of the light?

I cannot be sure but you have to believe me,
That strange things were happening in that breathing
    air,
My quick ears and eyes, they did not deceive me,
Some magic was there.

The Beach

Early morning, the sun but two hours old,
I walk, barefooted and alone, the blank sea-shore;
There are no leaping waves, no rough winds in the air,
The waveless waters lap the silent land.
The day's first tide moves in, bubbles and froth,
Soundlessly on my ear.
I keep to the broken edge
All the long way, leaving no footprints there,
Picking up pebbles, shining, cold,
Flinging them high and strong over the ribbed sand,
Hearing them plop in hidden pools among the rocks
In whose small depths the green crabs swim at peace,
Anemones sway, and black-eyed fish,
Like silver needles flash from side to side.
And now a squabbling gull is screaming overhead,
A yapping dog comes racing from the town;
I turn about and slowly make for home.

August Ends

A nip in the air today, and autumn
Playing hide and seek with summer;
Winter takes a first grip on plant, insect, bird.
Last blackberry flowers fade,
And fruit, moving from green to red,
Dangles foot long purple clusters
Over downy hedgerows, wasps go numb,
Fall drowsy on dropped plums, honey and smoky wax
Perfume the spidered loft, barley shines.
Swifts on curved wings wheel overhead
Printing broad arrows on the leaden sky;
And now I catch the echo of the far north wind
And over the shorn and stubbed land
The dreaded hawk hovers, and a cloud of peewits cry.

Mushrooms

Secret as toads. After a night's rain,
rise with the sun, dawn's flush on pillar and dome;
stronger than daisied turf, push into the light,
swell in an hour, tight, complete.
Summer's late harvest, miracles of white,
button up meadows, cool in the hill folds,
older than caveman wandering his wilderness.
Nothing more holy, live with manna's touch,
they shine, dew-crowned and comfortable.
And then, before final cockrow fades,
ungathered and overblown in every hiding place,
wearily topple over on blackened stalks,
drenched with decay, worms in the soggy flesh.
By afternoon, dwindled to dust,
the mystery gone with the dew.

Fog in November

Fog in November, trees have no heads,
Streams only sound, walls suddenly stop
Half-way up hills, the ghost of a man spreads
Dung on dead fields for next year's crop.
I cannot see my hand before my face,
My body does not seem to be my own,
The world becomes a far-off, foreign place,
People are strangers, houses silent, unknown.

Singing in the Streets

I had almost forgotten the singing in the streets,
Snow piled up by the houses, drifting
Underneath the door into the warm room,
Firelight, lamplight, the little lame cat
Dreaming in soft sleep on the hearth, mother dozing,
Waiting for Christmas to come, the boys and me
Trudging over blanket fields waving lanterns to the
    sky.
I had almost forgotten the smell, the feel of it all,
The coming back home, with girls laughing like stars,
Their cheeks, holly berries, me kissing one,
Silent-tongued, soberly, by the long church wall;
Then back to the kitchen table, supper on the white
    cloth,
Cheese, bread, the home-made wine,
Symbols of the night's joys, a holy feast.
And I wonder now, years gone, mother gone,
The boys and girls scattered, drifted away with the
    snowflakes,
Lamplight done, firelight over,
If the sounds of our singing in the streets are still
    there,
Those old tunes, still praising;
And now, a lifetime of Decembers away from it all,
A branch of remembering holly stabs my cheeks,
And I think it may be so;
Yes, I believe it may be so.

Montana Born

I saw her first through wavering candlelight,
My sister in her cradle, one hour old;
Outside, the snow was drifting through the night,
But she lay warm, oblivious to the cold.

Her eyes were closed, the half-moist wisps of hair,
A honey harvest on her wrinkled head,
The smile upon her face as if she was elsewhere,
But knew the land she had inherited.

My mother there at peace, her labour done,
Their greyness gone, her cheeks were coralline,
She welcomed me, her wondering first-born son
And placed my sister's new-nailed hand in mine.

I looked out through the freezing window pane,
The whitening acre bare and stretching far
That nine months hence would heave with swelling
  grain,
And over every distant peak a star.

And she, my winter sister, does she know
That all this homely countryside is hers,
Where once were warring Sioux and buffalo,
And covered waggons full of travellers?

But I will tell her all the Indian tales,
And show her grass-high fields, and sugar beet,
We'll ride all day along the western trails,
Missouri River glinting at our feet.

Montana born, she'll sleep beneath these beams,
And learn the simple ways, and say her prayers,
And even now she may see in her dreams
Another boy come climbing up the stairs.

The President

A sultry afternoon, late August,
travelling by train from St Louis, Missouri,
to stay with grandfather in Houston,
I fell asleep in the hot and chattering coach,
a few miles out of Springfield.
Suddenly woke when we slowed and stopped,
looked out, alarmed, from where I lolled,
read the name of the station staring there –
Dallas – and saw a President fall,
Dallas – the warm life drained from my cheeks,
my fourteen years rose in my throat;
the platform noises faded, I heard
those rifle-shots burst on my ears, one by one,
saw again the fatal air
that death-winged November morning
as through a haze of blood, the murdered motorcade
passing innocently down town, then Elm Street
running with grief and tears.

The train moved on into the soft Texan evening,
the sun painting every window red;
I carried the dark scene with me,
did not turn to summer sleep again,
remembering how in my fifth and quick-eyed year,
the President came to our small town,
the packed streets free as America.
My father held me high above the jostling crowds,
and sitting on his shoulders, the tall man came,
brown-haired and confident; I thought that day
he was some kind of God.

I called out 'Kennedy, Kennedy', and he
walked to me with blue and smiling eyes,
grasping my hand, and called me 'son',
and then was gone.

I think I cried that night in bed,
that I had seen the President face to face,
but now, just out of Dallas, cannot weep,
I only feel those peaceful fingers still,
his bullets buried in my heart.

Crown

Pick it up, and put it down,
it was once an old king's crown,
wore it on his whitening head
till an arrow struck him dead,
riding by himself, alas,
through a lonely mountain pass.
Ruler of a dozen lands,
thick dark forests, silver sands,
sailed his ships by many a shore,
farms and orchards by the score,
had a thousand flocks of sheep,
now his bones are buried deep
in a place that no one knows
but the rain and whirling snows,
and his eighty years are told
by this little round of gold;
though its magic has not gone,
do not try to put it on,
pick it up, and put it down,
it was once a sad king's crown.

The Quilt

That day we said goodbye to her,
Winter at work outside, the fire-flecked room
No louder than the black cat's purr
Breathing the way to her doom,
I saw it lying, solid and smooth there,
Her patchwork quilt,
A huge and dangling square,
Triangles of white, oblongs of red,
With bits from curtain and kilt.
I thought it looked just like
A landscape of little fields, seen
In springtime from an aeroplane,
Or, with dots of orange-green,
The mottled back of some big river pike.
And there were strips of calico in that counterpane,
Flannel from a grey Welsh shirt,
A blue velvet diamond, some sprigged lawn,
Faded pieces of a gingham skirt.
And as we slowly watched the dawn
Chequering the vast and empty sky,
'That was my wedding dress,' she softly said,
Placing her fingers on one silky hexagon;
She smiled, and finished with a sigh,
The fingers stiffened, the old head bowed.
Before we left, my grandmother had gone,
And married on that morning to the dead,
Lay calm and beautiful in her quilted shroud.

Button Box

An evening of wind and rain,
I found it on a shelf,
The button box, so full
Its lid would barely stay closed,
And opened it. Buttons.
Took them out one by one, all different
Shapes, sizes, colours, dull, thin;
Bone sometimes, and metal,
Holes, and none, some chipped,
A few leather, one had head of fox,
Another would do for dwarf's shield;
A dozen mother-of-pearl sang of the sea.
A set of silver ones
Might have been sixpences dancing,
A jet-black handful
Went to grandfather's funeral, two
Only from mother's wedding dress,
Tiny, pink as rosebuds.
I turned them over and over, those buttons,
Our family there, laid out in rows,
Dotting the table, reflections in lamplight,
Then put them back, boy, girl,
Man, woman, warm from my fingers,
Into their cramped box,
Counted raindrops.

Mole

Curled up in leafy fortress, secure,
I am the little black lord of the underworld,
proud and solitary in my tight plush;
prince of the sappers I have excavated the whole of
   Europe,
hills and tunnels advertising me all the way to Japan.
My four strong ounces drive forward at speed,
long, whiskered snout ramming the stones and roots,
leaving the damp night-tubes behind,
sun and wind unfriendly aliens
as I lift up the earth into the cruel light,
clawing out worms and grubs, gorging myself.

I do not see well but can sniff out stoats,
hear lightest footsteps hunting overhead,
will fight to the death with needle teeth,
once killed a sour king;
am not interested in my naked young.

Winter comes, I go down deeper
into my freezing element; do not sleep.
No fool, I am fearful of farmers, cunning traps,
the indignity of transfixion on bush and wire.

I am a strange character,
persistent and quarrelsome;
you would miss me though if I disappeared for ever
with dodo and dinosaur.
Better leave me alone to my dark moods.

Owls

They stare at you,
these ugly phantoms of the night,
and do not seem to care
if you stare back at them.
All day they perch, half asleep,
in lonely ruins, dark church towers,
not liking the sun,
dozing, and dreaming with stupid face,
of scurrying mice, fat beetles, baby birds,
swallowed greedily in one cruel gulp.

At twilight they come out.
Like floating paper glide along lanes,
noiselessly dipping over hedges,
or fanning their ghostly way
around the houses, down the avenues,
ears and eyes set for the kill.
Then, gorged with fresh meat,
they sag back home,
the moon's eye watching them,
hooting in the wind,
waiting for the next raw victim.

I do not like owls.
I shiver when I hear them
screeching at the bottom of the garden,
invading the darkness,
glad I'm not a mouse,
small bird or beetle.

Snail

Enjoys the damp. Remembers smell of sea.
Once moved with fish, swaying anemone,
the steady knock and whisper of the swell.
Coiled now in dead and mottled shell,
boneless and moist, peering with pimple-eyes,
creature of chilly dawn, the soft moonrise.
And with what slow and persevering toil
he plots his route along the easy soil,
sampling each tangled leaf and dewy stem,
writing in slimy signs his requiem,
until when summer's burning finger warns,
he probes the air with dry and anxious horns,
and then his final exploration past,
discards his china house and home at last.

The Hedger

Dawdling to school one chill morning
I watched the hedger at work
between Saunter's Patch and Bailey's Meadow.
Billhook in gloved hand,
gaitered, cloth cap on head,
he first trimmed the old hedge,
levelling the top with swift strokes,
the hook flashing, white chips flying,
his breath clouding the air.
Then plunged his hands into the thick growth,
cut out dead wood, brambles, hollow stems,
a blackbird's nest, memory of last year's spring,
trampled it underfoot in the ditch.

I waited alone in the lane
while he split the younger trees,
heard them creak and strain,
as he wove the branches, one by one,
in and out, to make the new hedge.

All day in school I worked with him,
that quiet hedger there, could not
settle to any lesson or book.

That evening on the way home,
I suddenly saw the whole hedge,
stretching the length of the long field,
I thought two dozen yards of it,
just right for size, so closely bound,
there was no gaping hole;
it was a wall of wood, tidy and clean,
rampart against cattle, sheep.
And over the hill I heard him still,
the hedger, chopping away in the fading light.

Charles

He was born blind with the snow on a winter's day;
The moon blank as marble stared at him from the full,
But his mother wept to see the vacant rolling of his
    eyes;
His father dared not look and despairingly turned
    away
When hands like feelers fumbled in space to pull
Fingers and lips to upturned face to recognize.
Growing older he sat in the dark learning voices by
    heart,
Carried on conversations with birds singing in summer
    trees,
Heard brooks changing their sound at floodtime, the
    angled dart
Of dazzled bats diving through twilight air.
But music played by wandering band or organ at the
    fair
Moved him to tears and fingers to invisible keys,
So that at twenty-five he began to drown the village
    church
With ceaseless tides of Handel, Bach and Mendelssohn,
And magnified the Lord for seven-and-thirty years.
With egg-shaped head he sat upright upon his perch,
Praying on flute we might depart in peace,
Triumphant came from Egypt on the bombardon,
Made thunderstorms at will, stars race like charioteers,
Captivity to turn, the harvest to increase;
He brought sweet healing to the troubled mind,
Fearlessly opened the eyes of the blind.

116

Dwarf

He hung about at corners, sat on walls,
Stared vacantly at nothing in the sky,
A squashed and waddling man with slobbering lips,
Big head, red eyes, and teeth askew,
A stunted Atlas holding up his trunk
On legs too squat for body's weight.
He held his arms wide open to embrace
The world but none would come within
To touch the furry moistness of his skin.
At times he wore upon his balding crown
A bowler hat with buckled, scurfy rim,
An old frock coat hung nearly to his feet
And string-bound spectacles cut in his nose.
He muttered to himself, he told the time
By blowing hard at dandelion clocks,
Whistled a snatch of melancholy tune
Then stopped to scratch his chin with broken nail
Or tug a raspberry ear, or slowly nod
When birds flew down to take his offered crumbs.
And when the organ played in church he danced
And beat his chest and laughed out loud,
And when he tried to catch with fluttering hands
The children on their way back home from school
They screamed and ran away from him.
But when he died his funeral stretched for miles,
No one remembered seeing such a throng,
The shops were shut, the town went out to weep;
His little grave was only four feet long
But love's sweet pity, oceans deep.

Glass

Will not bleed
But wounds when itself wounded,
outlives a generation, cracks
at a blow, sharp sound.
Older than the Pharaohs, bends
with furnace heat, polishes to ice surface,
screams at engraver's knife.
Backcloth for raindrops, frost crystals,
flying angels, saints in carmine,
all colours, and none,
will keep out angry voices, snow drifts.
Married to light, holds rainbows
in chandeliers, broken bottles, or show
delicate architecture of wasp's wing,
fault in bone, diamond;
can be a false jewel.
Glass gives new eyes, photographs of eyes,
prospect of life through an inch of it,
telescopes a dead star;
in league with sun will burn
forests and fields to loose ashes.
Milky, clear, solid as rock,
flowers to Venetian stem, gilt goblet,
hour glass on the run, bauble for Christmas,
dancing float, witches' ball.
The whole world is a house of glass;
we breathe our frail names on its cold face.

Echo

Walking for the first time
through a strange valley
a murmuring summer afternoon,
I cupped my hands, and shouted,
'Hello. Is anybody there?'
Back came a far-off echo
quivering on the small wind,
sighing among foxgloves and ferns,
'Hello. Is anybody there?'
as if seeking me out.

And returning that mild evening
along the deserted track,
stopped at the same place, and called,
'Hello. Is anybody there?'
but never an answer came,
no matter how many times I spoke;
there was only the hum of late bees
and a donkey braying on the slopes.

Where was echo?
Had it abandoned me?
What had I done to annoy?
Or was there no echo coming that way?

But it was like talking to someone
who does not want to speak,
content to be silent sometimes.

De la Mare's Bell

This was de la Mare's bell,
Brass, reflecting what it imaged,
Minute, distorted, upside down,
The handle, a black minaret on its tower,
Its tiny tongue,
Time's clapper, tinkling like glass inside.

It used to rest on the table by his bed,
With flowers, a clock, and books
Unopened or half read.
I often saw him lift it gently up,
The old fingers twining round the wood,
Then shake it into dulcimer sound,
Very kind and pleasant to the ear,
Its voice chiming clearly through the Twickenham
    house;
A few charmed seconds, and then
The bell was brought to dumbness, the air was still,
The Roman head sank back to rest;
It was all over.

And I used to think how like de la Mare his bell was,
Fragile, haunting, sure, precise,
Sounding boards for dream and the indefinable.
And now, de la Mare dead, the flowers dead,
The clock counting out life elsewhere,
My son rings the bell,
Rings it, not for a poet's passing or curfew for night,
Rings it, innocent bellman, through childhood's frail
    house,

Through twilight, moonlight, the soft shades,
Listening forests of stars,
The dusty pavilions of Time.
But, O, if I rang till doomsday's crack
I could not bring him back.
Let this blithe bellman ring.

PHOEBE HESKETH

Phoebe Hesketh was both in Preston, Lancashire, in 1909, and educated at Cheltenham Ladies College. She was married in 1931, and had three children. During the war she was woman's page editor of the *Bolton Evening News*, and then worked in freelance journalism. She had eleven volumes of poetry published between 1948 and 1988, and three prose works. In the 1950s she became an active member of PEN and a Fellow of the Royal Society of Literature. She lectured in General Studies at the Womens College, Bolton, for three years. She has twice won the Poetry Society Greenwood Prize, and in 1988 she won first prize in an International Poetry Competition. Her collected and new poems, *Netting the Sun*, will be published by Enitharmon in 1989. Her published poetry includes *Lean Forward Spring* (Sidgwick and Jackson, 1948), *No Time For Cowards* (Heinemann, 1952), *Out of the Dark* (Heinemann, 1954), *Between Wheels and Stars* (Heinemann, 1956), *The Buttercup Children* (Hart-Davis, 1958), *Prayer For Sun* (Hart-Davis, 1966), *A Song of Sunlight* (Chatto & Windus, Chatto Poets for the Young, 1974), *Preparing to Leave* (Enitharmon, 1977), *The Eighth Day* (Enitharmon, 1980), *Over The Brook* (Taxus, 1986), *Netting the Sun* (Enitharmon, 1989). Her published prose includes *My Aunt Edith* (Peter Davies, 1966) and *Rivington* (Peter Davies, 1972).

On a hot day in the middle of June 1988, I travelled north to a village in Lancashire to meet Phoebe Hesketh. She was waiting for me on the platform, looking cool and attractive in her cotton dress and straw hat.

Phoebe's bungalow is filled with books, pictures, cards and interesting ornaments, and has a comfortable, welcoming feeling. There are cows in the field at the end of her back garden, and she grows old-fashioned flowers like lupins and antirrhinums. The buttercups at the bottom of the garden seemed just right for a poet who has written 'The Buttercup Children'.

She was born in Preston, Lancashire, where her father pioneered the first Department of Radiology in Britain. Her mother played the violin in the Hallé Orchestra. From the start she enjoyed poetry, and remembers Robert Louis Stevenson's *A Child's Garden of Verses* being a favourite collection. Her own writing began early and she was able to quote from memory:

> The red leaves of Autumn
> Have perished on the ground,
> The birds have flown to warmer lands,
> The flowers are sleeping sound.

By the age of eleven she had written enough material to fill *A Book of Poems* by Phoebe Rayner (her maiden name) and had also won several writing competitions. At Cheltenham Ladies College, her English teacher (with the rather grand name of Miss Winnington-Ingram) ordered the girls to 'write a Petrarchan sonnet', and then pronounced '*Yours* is really good, Phoebe!'

Because of her mother's fatal illness, Phoebe had to leave school at seventeen. She married young, and combined her domestic life with horse-riding (she has always had a passion for horses, and misses them dreadfully now), some writing and plenty of reading. She was soon contributing poems and articles to magazines. Her advice to any young, would-be writer is to 'read as widely and as much as you can.'

We talked about poets and share some favourites, particularly Robert Frost, the American poet, and Edward Thomas – a poster of his poem 'Tall Nettles' graces Phoebe's loo door; I have the same one in my hallway. Of living poets she admires R. S. Thomas.

People and places have always been important. One memorable relative was her father's suffragette sister, who springs marvellously to life in Phoebe's biography *My Aunt Edith*. Rivington in Lancashire is of special importance. There Phoebe and her husband Aubrey lived for more than forty years in the beautiful Georgian Fisher House. Her book, *Rivington*, tells the story of the village and their life there. Their three children were born in Rivington. First Martin, her quiet and reserved architect son; next Richard, who had a tree-house and liked sleeping outside in his tent; and then Catherine. Sadly, Richard was drowned at school, when his parents were away on the island of Iona. Phoebe told me of the dreadful moment when a shepherd broke the news of the accident, and she has written most movingly about Richard in *Boy Drowning*.

Life hasn't always been easy. Her husband's death after a long illness left her widowed a few years ago. Catherine now lives in America, so Phoebe can't see much of her grandchildren. She no longer lives in Fisher House. Yet I had the impression of a busy, involved person, working with a writers' workshop (she is an experienced lecturer and course tutor), preparing for a collected edition of her poems, writing to friends, reading avidly, and in touch with today's literature. Freelance work has led to editing the woman's page of a newspaper, giving poetry readings, and broadcasting.

Her writing shows no signs of strain or pretension; it is graceful and natural, varied in subject and vocabulary. She has drawn on a lifetime's experience of people and the countryside: 'Tom Rich' *was* the family gardener; a friend *was* ill in 'Ward F 4'; she *did* look through 'A Train Window in Lincolnshire' (while travelling with another poet, Stevie Smith).

When I asked her how she would feel about this book being dedicated to Walter de la Mare, she said: 'Oh, I like his work so much . . . and I wish I'd met him.' She quoted the opening of his poem 'Autumn' to me . . . 'There is a wind where the rose was . . .'

I can't resist ending with one of Phoebe Hesketh's favourite quotations: 'Education begins when you've forgotten what you were taught.'

Ducks

A small procession waddles single file
Along the narrow lane:
With sure, sea-rolling gait
Like happy sailors home in port again,
Six white ducks lumber on;
And barge-like, broad and slow,
With orange paddles, through the mud they go.
Fat cobblestones they ride
As high white horses on a heaving tide;
And must negotiate
An awkward gate.
Across a field with swaying, rhythmic beat,
They breast the air as though
There is a sea below,
Yet orderly in line,
They keep their course till water is in sight:
Then quacking in delight,
With heads down, wings unfurled,
They leave the muddy edge –
Each trails a wrinkled wedge
Across the glassy pond disturbing there
The mirrored scene where clouds and tree tops float,
And cattle stand and stare.

Cats

Cats are contradictions; tooth and claw
Velvet-padded;
Snowflake-gentle paw
A fist of pins;
Kettles on the purr
Ready to spit;
Black silk, then bristled fur.

Cats are of the East –
Scimitar and sphinx;
Sunlight striped with shade.
Leopard, lion, lynx
Moss-footed in a frightened glade;
Slit eyes an amber glint
Of boring through the darkness cool as jade.

Cats have come to rest
Upon the cushioned West,
Here, dyed-in-the-silk,
They lap up bottled milk –
And that of human kindness –
And return
To the mottled woods of Spring
Making the trees afraid
With leaf and wing
A-flutter at the movement of the fern.

Midnight-wild
With phosphorescent eyes,
Cats are morning-wise
Sleeping as they stare into the sun,
Blind to the light,
Deaf to echoing cries,
From a ravaged wood
Cats see black and white,
Morning and night as one.

The Fox

It was twenty years ago I saw the fox
Gliding along the edge of prickling corn,
A nefarious shadow
Between the emerald field and bristling hedge,
On velvet feet he went.

The wind was kind, withheld from him my scent
Till my threaded gaze unmasked him standing there,
The colour of last year's beech-leaves, pointed black,
Poised, uncertain, quivering nose aware
Of danger throbbing through each licking leaf.
One foot uplifted, balanced on the brink
Of perennial fear, the hunter hunted stood.

I heard no alien stir in the friendly wood,
But the fox's sculpted attitude was tense
With scenting, listening, with a seventh sense
Flaring to the alert; I heard no sound
Threaten the morning; and followed his amber stare,
But in that hair-breadth moment, that flick of the eye,
He vanished.

And now, whenever I hear the expectant cry
Of hounds on the empty air,
I look to a gap in the hedge and see him there
Filling the space with fear; the trembling leaves
Are frozen in his stillness till I hear
His leashed-up breathing – how the stretch of time
Contracts within the flash of re-creation!

Lakeland Fox

Red as autumn bracken
rust on a plough
iron in the river,
I'm hunted by a mottled pack
hand-fed, sheltered, kept to no end
but the end of me
their wild, lithe brother, free-
running as a mountain stream.

Now, wearing the grey
of dust, not age, I glare
from seasoned wood engraved
with my date and place.
Nose wrinkled in snarling rage,
my yellow glass eyes
stare out loud at passers-by.

My breath smoked on the mothering fell;
I was torn in seven pieces
twitching in the bloodied hush
before mask, pads, and brush were knifed
for the chosen,
my body flung with orgasmic yell
to the dogs.

Thrush

Timorously I write about the thrush –
for all's been written before.
But this one makes a chair of a laurel bush,
And hops till the lawn becomes a dancing-floor.
Tuning-in to earth he hears worms talk –
pink corkscrews burrowing a twisted way
up instead of down: he stabs the cork,
stands back and pulls; gobbles a wriggling prey.
Then blinking the one boot-button eye we see,
swallows, pauses, dives into a tree.

Owl

The owl's a clock-face without fingers,
two keyholes for seeing,
striking silent as frost.

Soft, white as first snow
its flight is a wash
through trees without flicker of leaf,
a pocket of air
bulging with warm, swallowed blood.

Out there, the wood grown stiller
than winter with spring breathing bluebells and fern under cover;
each feather pinned; fur and whisker
twitching in windless night.
And Time flying white from the clock-tower
screeching the hour of death.

The Buttercup Children

Down the dusty lane of Summer,
Thick with scent, tangled with honeysuckle,
The children come so slowly
You'd think the afternoon would lie for ever
Sleeping along the hedges without shadow.

School is the past; tomorrow is only a name,
And sorrow has no share in this enchantment.
They live in the immediate delight
Of butterflies and clocks of dandelion –
Blown as soon as looked at, without time
To jostle them from one thought to another.

Theirs is the present
Wide open as a daisy to the sun;
They do not bruise it in their gathering.
What though these shining buttercup bouquets
Droop in their eager hands?
The gold ungrudging petals drop behind
Uncounted through a timeless afternoon.

Boy Drowning

Drowning is pushing through
a barrier like birth
only the elements are exchanged:
air for water.
Then, water for air,
my lungs
folded flat as butterflies' wings
struggled to expand
in a round scream.

Now I make no sound –
or they don't hear
water damming my ear-
drums, nostrils, eyes –
I fight like a salmon on grass
choked with a bubble.
I cannot rise
a third time.

Sally

She was a dog-rose kind of girl:
elusive, scattery as petals;
scratchy sometimes, tripping you like briars.
She teased the boys
twisting this way and that, not to be tamed
or taught any more than the wind.
Even in school the word 'ought'
had no meaning for Sally.
On dull days
she'd sit quiet as a mole at her desk
delving in thought.
But when the sun called
she was gone, running the blue day down
till the warm hedgerows prickled the dusk
and moths flickered out.

Her mother scolded; Dad
gave her the hazel-switch,
said her head was stuffed with feathers
and a starling tongue.
But they couldn't take the shine out of her.
Even when it rained
you felt the sun saved under her skin.
She'd a way of escape
laughing at you from the bright end of a tunnel,
leaving you in the dark.

Boy With Kite

I am master of my kite, and
the wind tugs against me
on blue ropes of air.
Above tasselled trees
my kite glides and swoops,
pink-and-yellow falcon surging loose
from my tight fist.

White string bites
into flesh, my wrist
flexes like a falconer's.

I am dancing with my kite
heel-and-toe to earth,
body braced
against the fleet north-easter laced
with fraying clouds.

Lifted steeple-clear
of church and school and hill
I am master of my world.

Paint Box

He tried to tell them what he felt,
could say it only in colours –
Sunday's white page shading to grey
of evening clocks and bells-in-the-rain.
Monday morning, bright yellow brass
of a cock crowing.
Story-time, purple.
Scarlet is shouting in the playground.

His world's a cocoon
round as an egg, an acorn
sprouting green.
The schoolroom square and hard,
his desk hard and square
facing the enemy blackboard.

'You must learn to read,' they said
and gave him a painting-book alphabet.
Apple swelled beautifully red. Balloon
expanded in blue.
C was a cage for a bird;
his brush wavered through
painting himself
a small brown smudge inside.

Truant

Sing a song of sunlight
My pocket's full of sky –
Starling's egg for April
Jay's feather for July.
And here's a thorn bush three bags full
Of drift-white wool.

They call him dunce, and yet he can discern
Each mouse-brown bird,
And call its name and whistle back its call,
And spy among the fern
Delicate movement of a furred
Fugitive creature hiding from the day.
Discovered secrets magnify his play
Into a vocation.

Laughing at education
He knows where the redshank hides her nest, perceives
a red-patch tremble when a coot lays seige
To water territory.
Nothing escapes his eye:
A ladybird
Slides like a blood-drop down a spear of grass;
The sapphire sparkle of a dragon-fly
Redeems a waste of weeds.
Collecting acorns, telling the beads of the year
On yew tree berries, his mind's too full for speech.

Back in the classroom he can never find
Answers to dusty questions, yet could teach,
Deeper than knowledge,
Geometry of twigs
Scratched on a sunlit wall;
History in stones,
Seasons told by the fields' calendar –
Living languages of Spring and Fall.

Ward F 4

There is no weather in my room,
a white cube, bare
except for a bedside chest; one chair.
The window behind my bed
looks blind on a blind wall,
but I cannot turn my head.

No sky; no sun;
one lamp with hard green shade
is my daylight
and nightlight.
(No flowers, please, nowhere
to put them but on the floor.)
I face the brown door, stare
at the black knob, waiting . . .

Nurses come and go
brisk, kind under crackling starch.
They give me pills, injections
with cheerful remarks about the weather.
But there is no weather in my room.

For twelve months I have not seen a tree
or a patch of grass.
I think I could walk again
if I saw grass.
I shut my eyes.
I can see more with my eyes shut –
heather, a bright stream,
the flash of a bird.

143

Autumn, Winter have wasted away;
today is the first day of Spring;
and nurse says the sun is shining . . .
My splints are off;
my limbs feel supple
and I'm running over grass
where the willow lets down her yellow hair.

Toffee-brown chestnut buds unclose
fingers soft as silver-fox.
There's movement among branches: a speckled thrush
swings and sings, frilling the needled larch
with promised green.
Blossom and cloud pile high, higher as I pass.
I am free; the grass is warm,
yielding to my feet . . .

The door opens and the doctor comes in
returning me to the white cube.
He talks of tests and treatment,
makes no promises.
Improvement is slow.

Visitors come and go
bringing rain on their coats
or a bunch of flowers –
only they bring the weather into my room.
But when they've gone
I'm more alone than before
waiting, watching the door.
The clock ticks on.

Tom Rich

Tom Rich, the gardener,
has a strawberry mark on his face;
his hands are wide enough to span
the fattest vegetable-marrow.
With shirt-sleeves rolled,
forearm muscles swelled,
he pushes his comrade barrow to feed the roses.

In April sun he prunes each bush
deftly as a hairdresser
with skilful secateurs.
On the backs of his hands the straw-gold hairs
glint among foxy freckles.
Now he is planting out
seedlings pale from confinement
in the potting-shed:
the crooked, cumbrous fingers
approaching with gargantuan love
take each one gently as a dove
carrying home a feather to her nest.

Slowly he weeds the border,
his large boots
moving like careful barges near the roots
of coltness gem.
His giant shadow falls
where lilliputian ferns are waving
green signals to the butterflies:
cabbage-whites on dusty wings
zigzag away, and booming bees

dizzying in-and-out of early flowers,
drugged with laburnum showers,
mumble in nectar-drunken drone
at his approach.

A carvanning snail with silver trail
removes its home to safety at the edge
of the strong box-hedge.
But not a violet need shield its head –
this grandson of Colossus
moves carefully as a deer
picking a dry-foot way among damp mosses.

Tom with his strawberry-face is rooted
strong as a tree in the garden.
And faithful like the robin
he never deserts
when the sundial's capped with snow,
but stays around, warming his hands and his dinner
at the outhouse fire,
throwing crumbs to the birds,
sharing their patience.

Old Woman

Now she is old and frayed
From years of chopping sticks and baking bread,
Her twisted hands lie still.
Children's voices shouting on the hill
Fall quiet on her ears.
And from her tread the willow spring has gone.
Eyes once quick as thorns
Are dim with mist and dreams and distances.

Gathering Sticks

Crackle-footed, gathering sticks she goes
This veiled November morning;
Bent as a thorn tree, fingers crooked as twigs,
She scrabbles among dead leaves.
But her scarlet cap is brighter than beaded hips
On a naked briar.

All her life she's drawn her strength from trees,
Answered the pull of Spring –
That green rope tugging the spirit from kitchen cares.
Now caught by a spider's thread, she's drawn
To an ancient blood-tie with this autumn wood
Where the year is burning down through the ember-red
Of berries and bramble leaves.

A rattling thistle scratches the empty air,
And rosebay hosts
Unplumed by the snatching wind are delicate ghosts –
Seed in the earth and no more share in growth.
But she with a shoulder of sticks has a fire to mend
And time by the autumn sun is not to be lost;
She will not wait for the velvet-fingered dark
To snare her purpose in a net of frost.

Yew Tree Guest House

In guest-house lounges
elderly ladies shrivel away
wearing bright beads and jumpers
to colour the waiting day
between breakfast and bed.

Grey widows whose beds and meals are made,
husbands tidied with the emptied cupboards,
live in mortgaged time
disguising inconsequence
with shavings of surface talk, letters
to nieces, stitches dropped in the quick-knit jacket,
picked up for makeweight meaning.

Weekdays are patterned by meals –
sole chance for speculation –
will it be cabbage or peas; boiled fish or fried?
Dead Sunday is dedicated to roast beef –
knives and forks are grips upon existence.
This diversion lengthens the journey;
and since Mrs Porter ceased to come downstairs,
ceased altogether,
the ladies at the Yew Tree Guest House
draw closer to the table.

Geriatric Ward

Feeding time in the geriatric ward;
I wondered how they found their mouths,
and seeing that not one looked up, inquired
'Do they have souls?'

'If I had a machine-gun,' answered the doctor
'I'd show you dignity in death instead of living death.
Death wasn't meant to be kept alive,
but we're under orders
to pump blood and air in after the mind's gone.
I don't understand souls;
I only learned about cells
law-abiding as leaves
withering under frost.
But we, never handing over
to Mother who knows best,
spray cabbages with oxygen, hoping for a smile,
count pulses of breathing bags whose direction is lost,
and think we've won.

Here's a game you can't win –
one by one they ooze away in the cold.
There's no society forbidding
detention of the old.'

The Frog Prince

He was cold as slime,
Coloured to the underside
Of a rotted leaf
Mottled brown and yellow.

With promises of princehood underneath
The skin – if warmed by love –
He chose my pillow
For his transformation,
Croaked at me to stroke his throat
Pulsing like a swamp-bubble.

Pity froze to contempt;
Rather than touch him I lifted the pillow,
Flung him into the night.
Now alone in autumn mood I wonder
Who is this tall young man
Supple as willow and wind,
Carrying the sun on his shoulder.
His light shafts through me to its mark
In a girl not beautiful but kind.

Myth

She felt herself a white mouse
treading the mill of getting up
getting to bed, grinding the daily trivia
into daily bread,
turning out turning in
turning round in the spin
of days and nights and days.

So she turned herself into a horse
winged beyond concrete and routine
grazing the grass of Parnassus,
kicking up dust among stars,
feathering the wind,
leaping a rainbow to land
in her native sea,
printing the sand with hooves
where blood-drops sprang
filling her veins with quicksilver life.

Going Away and Returning

The best of going away is the going –
That inland sea view
Glimpsed through gaps in a traffic queue;
White mosques on stilts of a pier striding
Towards empty horizons blue with dreaming.

Jolted, we arrive
At Bella Vista gleaming
Gull-grey on a grey parade
Where tired waves at high-tide flap-
Flop, slopping on grey stones.

Later the swept shore is sad
With deck-chair sleepers, paddling children, mad
Mothers grabbing infants from the sea,
Couples linked by hoarse transistors,
Picnic-papers,
Castles built to be washed away,
And shells,
Scoured, gathered, taken home
To a blind house that smells
Of lack and damp.

Return is dead flowers
In the same vase;
That letter unanswered on the fridge;
Floor unswept;
Clock stopped; range
Cold – the worst of coming back is the kept
Secret of a locked house,
Ourselves on the outside, strange.

From a Train Window in Lincolnshire

Green miles of rye and barley,
Gold, green of mustard, kale
Flank sun-tanned farms and houses
By riverside and rail –
No railings, walls, or hedges;
The train slides through the sun
Past Stickney, Trumble Woodside
And Coningsby, to run
By marsh and mere and willow,
Across unfeatured fen
And fields where men are hoeing,
Where scarecrows jerk, and then
Stand stiff and still, sleeves flapping,
Outstaring birds and men.

We Must Drive On

Across our path
As we speed north
The red deer leap – one, two, three.
We stop, exclaim at the antlered stag
And his shadowy hinds, but must drive on.
No time to follow that retreat
Through beech-mast brown on velvet feet,
No time to linger under leaves
Before the Autumn whirls them down.
And though this will not happen again –
The moment of the three red deer
Crossing the russet of the year,
And you and I together here,
We must drive on.

Snow

It is snowing
no sound
flakes spelling
patterns
dumb ground staring
　Air feather-headed
　　loosing words
　　　everywhere
　　　　unheard

RUSSELL HOBAN

Russell Hoban was born in 1925 in Lansdale, Pennsylvania. He attended the Philadephia Museum School of Industrial Art from 1941 to 1943 and was in the army from 1943 to 1945, serving in the Infantry in the Italian Campaign.

From 1945 to 1957 he had a succession of twenty-one different jobs in New York City, including Western Union messenger, shipping clerk, freight handler, display artist, film animator, and TV art director at an advertising agency. He was a freelance illustrator from 1957 to 1965 and an advertising copywriter from 1965 to 1967. Since 1967 he has been a full-time fiction writer. He has lived in London since 1969. His novel *Riddley Walker* won the John W. Campbell Memorial Award in 1982 and the Australian Science Fiction Achievement Award in 1983. *How Tom Beat Captain Najork and his Hired Sportsmen* (Jonathan Cape) won the 1974 Whitbread Children's Book Award.

The Mouse and his Child (Faber and Faber, 1967) was his first novel. His other novels are *The Lion of Boaz-Jachin and Jachin-Boaz* (1973), *Kleinzeit* (1974), *Turtle Diary* (1975), *Riddley Walker* (1980), *Pilgermann* (1983) and *The Medusa Frequency* (1987). All published by Jonathan Cape. He has written fifty-two picture books, which include *Dinner at Alberta's* (Jonathan Cape, 1977; Puffin, 1980), *Bedtime for Frances* (Faber and Faber, 1960), *How Tom beat Captain Najork and His Hired Sportsmen* (Jonathan Cape, 1974) and *The Marzipan Pig* (Jonathan Cape, 1986; Puffin, 1988), and two books of verse for children.

Russell Hoban was surprised, though I think pleased, to be included in a poetry collection. He simply didn't think of himself as a poet, although several poems of his have been anthologized and his book, *The Pedalling Man*, was popular and should not have been allowed to go out of print. And, poet or not, he handed me some unpublished poems, and editors are always greedy for these.

As a child, he enjoyed memorizing poetry, and can still quote reams from Sir Walter Scott's 'Lay of the Last Minstrel' and 'Lady of the Lake'.

He is an American, but has lived in England since 1969. He was so good at drawing by the age of five that his parents hoped he would become an artist. But he was good with words, too, and at high school he won prizes for writing and poetry. He left Temple University, Philadelphia, after only five weeks, then studied at art school for eighteen months. He served in the Infantry in the Second World War, and there then followed a succession of jobs. He worked as a Western Union messenger, in a display studio, in an electro-plating factory, in a silk-screen printing studio, and on several magazines. Later he was a film animator and a TV art director in advertising. He was a freelance magazine illustrator for a while, and an advertising copywriter before becoming a full-time writer.

I was fascinated to look through a portfolio of his artwork – very bold, sinewy drawings, some of men working, and boxing. It was dynamic stuff, very compelling. But now, he told me, writing is his life, so we began to discuss writing. Russell Hoban doesn't feel he has

159

actually been influenced by anyone, but does feel standards were set for him by particular writers like Dickens and Joseph Conrad. His taste for the supernatural has led him to an appreciation of M. R. James, Algernon Blackwood, Lafcadio Hearn, Arthur Machin and Oliver Onions. He enjoys Oscar Wilde and Walter de la Mare's stories, and thinks he himself inhabits in writing a territory not unlike de la Mare's – 'It's a question of the recognized actual and the actual actual,' he explained. He reads de la Mare stories to his three youngest sons, Jachin, Ben and Wieland. One writer he introduced I didn't know, the American H. P. Lovecraft. The blurb inside one of his books claimed: 'You are about to enter a new dimension of utmost terror.' I closed it quickly.

Russell Hoban and his family live in a small Victorian house in Fulham, south west London. The room we talked in was one of the liveliest I've seen. The walls were filled with books on various subjects – birds, art, music, mathematics, animals, literature. A word-processor and piles of files and paper inhabited one area, and the room also housed puppets, paper mobiles, a red dragon and coloured lanterns. He was in the middle of two pieces of work – a new adult novel to follow such successes as *Riddley Walker* and *Turtle Diary*, and a new children's picture book. He's a man who works extremely hard. His ambition, he told me, is always the same: 'To finish the book I'm working on at present.'

Inevitably I asked about *The Mouse and his Child*, a favourite among my friends and family, and an acknowledged classic in the tradition of *Alice* and *The Wind in the Willows*. To my delight, he showed me the original tin pair of mice in their neat felt clothes; they still wind

160

up and make their circular movement. Straight from the store, too, came 'the little tin seal who balanced a red and yellow ball on his nose.' He has quite a collection of tin wind-up toys and is fascinated by them.

Russell Hoban's poems cover a wide range of mood and subjects. Some of the earlier, lighter ones come from his charming stories of badger Frances, her sister, Gloria, and friend Thelma; I think they stand alone too, for their grace and wit, their lack of any condescension. He really knows children, understands the best friend who can be a pain, the annoying small sister, the secret friend ('Skilly Oogan' was invented by his daughter Julia), learning to ride a bicycle (Esme is another daughter). There really was a 'Pedalling Man' weathervane, and 'Solu the Barber' really existed too. In fact, he worked in the Puerto Rican quarter of New York City which Russell used to frequent for ideas for Rheingold beer radio ads. In contrast come the fantasy worlds of 'At Dimla' and the 'Rendezvous at Zarmni', flowing poetic pieces with an underlying darkness, and also the evocative prose poem written for his daughter Phoebe because she listened to 'What the Wind Said'.

I asked Russell Hoban for his thoughts on children and poetry. He feels they should find their own way towards reading and writing it, without being too influenced and too pushed.

One memory of my visit will be a delicious gingerbread man baked by his wife, Gundula. It reminded me to find out the background to the 'Lorna Doone' poem. It seems that in the States there was a cookie assortment called this, and the plainest biscuits had the name embossed on them. It makes an intriguing poem, anyway, and I hope I'm right in believing that more poetry will come from Russell Hoban in the future.

161

Skilly Oogan

Skilly Oogan's no one you can see,
And no one else can be his friend but me.
Skilly lives where swallows live, away up high
Beneath the topmost eaves against the sky.
When all the world's asleep on moonlit nights,
Up on our roof he flies his cobweb kites.
He has an acorn boat that, when it rains,
He sails in gutters, even down the drains.
Sometimes he hides in letters that I write –
Snug in the envelope and out of sight,
On six-cent stamps he travels in all weathers
And with the midnight owl returns on silent feathers.
In summer time he rides the dragonflies
Above the pond, and looks in bullfrogs' eyes
For his reflection when he combs his hair.
And sometimes when I want him he's not there;
But mostly Skilly Oogan's where I think he'll be,
And no one even knows his name but me.

The Pedalling Man

We put him on the roof and we painted him blue,
And the pedalling man knew what to do –
He just pedalled, yes he pedalled:
He rode through the night with the wind just right
And he rode clear into the morning,
Riding easy, riding breezy, riding
Slow in the sunrise and the wind out of the east.

A weathervane was what he was –
Cast-iron man with a sheet-iron propeller, riding a
Worm gear, holding a little steering wheel,
Iron legs pumping up and down – show him a
Wind and he'd go. Work all day and
All his pay was the weather. Nights, too,
We'd lie in bed and hear him
Creak up there in the dark as he
Swung into the wind and worked up speed,
Humming and thrumming so you could
Feel it all through the house –
The more wind, the faster he went, right through
Spring, summer, and fall.

He rode warm winds out of the south,
Wet winds out of the east, and the
Dry west winds, rode them all with a
Serious iron face. Hard-nosed, tight-mouthed
Yankee-looking kind of an iron man.
'Show me a wind and I'll go,' he said.
'I'm a pedalling fool and I'm heading for weather.'
The weather came and he kept on going, right into

Winter, and the wind out of the north and no let-up –
We lived on a hill, and wind was what we got a lot of.

Then a night came along, and a blizzard was making,
Windows rattling and the whole house shaking,
But the iron man just hummed with the blast,
Said, 'Come on, wind, and come on fast,
Show me your winter, make it nice and cool,
Show me your weather – I'm a pedalling fool!'
Gears all spinning, joints all shivering,
Sheet-iron clattering, cast-iron quivering till WHOMP!
The humming stopped, and we all sat up in bed with
Nothing to listen to but the wind right through into
    morning.

And there he was when we dug him out, propeller all
    bent,
One eye in the snow and one eye
Staring up at the sky, still looking for weather.
He never let on he was beat, not him.

Well, my father put him up on the roof again, this time
Without the propeller.
'Let him ride easy,' he said. 'A man can only take
Just so much north wind, even if he's iron.'

Original Tin

The sky is tin, the street is tin, and now
a tin man, red and yellow walking as a spring un-
   winds.
His two halves do not fit exactly but
he perseveres and finds a house of tin on which
are printed red bricks, blue windows,
and the picture of a door at which he knocks
(no answer), says in his tin voice,
'I'm here,' then enters.
Now his face is printed on the printed windows
looking out past slanting lines of white. 'I'm here,'
he says in his tin voice, and notes the rattling of the
   sky.

The Tin Frog

I have hopped, when properly wound up, the whole
   length
Of the hallway; once hopped half-way down the stairs,
   and fell.
Since then the two halves of my tin have been awry;
   my strength
Is not quite what it used to be; I do not hop so well.

Solu the Barber

I know a barber named Solu.
The words he speaks are soft and few;
He nods to me and says hello
Because his place is where I go
For haircuts now.

With comb and scissors through the day
He works, then puts his tools away,
Cleans up the shop, sweeps up the hair,
Sits down in his own barber chair
And rests awhile.

He takes down from its little shelf
A small guitar he made himself
And while the city evening brings
Its lamplight to the street he sings
Of islands far.

I know him just to say hello
But not quite well enough to go
Inside to listen to his song,
So on the street I linger long
Outside his door.

Sometimes I sit across the way
Not close enough to hear him play,
But in the lighted window there
I see him singing in his chair
With his guitar.

His lips move while his fingers strum
And soft beneath my breath I hum
And wonder to what tropic harbour
On music sails Solu the barber.

The Empty House

Where the lone wind on the hilltop
Shakes the thistles as it passes,
Stirs the quiet-ticking grasses
That keep time outside the door,
Stands a house that's grey and silent;
No one lives there any more.

Wending through the broken windows,
Every season and its weather
Whisper in those rooms together:
Summer's warm and wandering rains
Rot the leaves of last year's autumn,
Warp the floors that winter stains.

In a papered hall a clock-shape,
Dim and pale on yellowed flowers,
Still remains where rang the hours
Of a clock that's lost and gone.
And the fading ghost keeps no-time
On the wall it lived upon.

On a stairway where no footsteps
Stir the dusty sunlight burning
Sit the patient shadows turning
Speechless faces to the wall
While they hear the silent striking
Of that no-clock in the hall.

'Dawn of no-time! Noon of no-time!'
Cries the phantom echo chiming,
And the shadows, moving, miming,
Slowly shift before the light.
But no eye has seen their motion
When the clock says, 'No-time night!'

No eye has seen them dancing
In their blackness fell and bright,
To a silent tune
In the dark of the moon
When the clock sings no-time night.

Gloria, My Little Sister

Gloria, my little sister —
Well, I guess I would have missed her
If there hadn't ever been a
Gloria my little sister.

She's the one they all like better,
She's the one that gets the most.
When she stays up late they let her
Make a mess with cinnamon toast.
I get spanked if I just twist her
Arm, that little Gloria sister.
Still, I guess I would have missed her.

No one ever thinks she's tricky.
She spilled honey on the floor —
Mother found me very sticky.
Gloria was out the door.
When I caught her no one hit her.
I got spanked because I bit her
Ear, that little Gloria sister.
Still, I guess I would have missed her.

She can hardly throw a ball,
She can't ever catch at all.
Father said that I was mean
When my ball went through the screen
Door because she stepped aside.
Mother kissed her when she cried.
I was sorry that I missed her,
Gloria my little sister.

Brothers would have been all right.
Brothers help you in a fight,
Brothers put your worms on hooks,
Brothers lend you comic books.
Why can't fathers, why can't mothers
Give us large and useful brothers?
Still, I guess I would have missed her,
Gloria my little sister.

Funeral

Gloria and I have often,
Walking slowly, singing steady,
With a shoebox for a coffin,
Buried neighbours who were ready.

Harold Woodmouse, Bertha Toad
(One a cat killed, one a dog)
On the hillside near the road
Sleep along with Herman Frog.

In our funeral today,
Going to his final rest:
Buster William Henry Jay,
Fallen lately from the nest.

Not quite old enough to fly,
Barely big enough to die –
In the hillside here we lay
Buster William Henry Jay.

Homework

Homework sits on top of Sunday, squashing Sunday flat.
Homework has the smell of Monday, homework's very fat
Heavy books and piles of paper, answers I don't know.
Sunday evening's almost finished, now I'm going to go
Do my homework in the kitchen. Maybe just a snack,
Then I'll sit right down and start as soon as I run back
For some chocolate sandwich cookies. Then I'll really do
All that homework in a minute. First I'll see what new
Show they've got on television in the living room.
Everybody's laughing there, but misery and gloom
And a full refrigerator are where I am at.
I'll just have another sandwich. Homework's very fat.

Lorna Doone
Last Cookie Song
(*I Shared It With Gloria*)

All the sandwich cookies sweet
In their frilly paper neat,
They are gone this afternoon,
They have left you, Lorna Doone.

Lorna Doone, Lorna Doone,
Roaming through the heather,
Lorna Doone, Lorna Doone,
We'll grow old together.

Chocolate and vanilla creams
Pass like little tasty dreams,
Eaten up and gone too soon,
All but you, our Lorna Doone.

You are plain and you are square
And your flavour's only fair.
Soon there'll be an empty place
Where we saw your smiling face.

Lorna Doone, Lorna Doone,
You were last but you weren't wasted.
Lorna Doone, Lorna Doone,
We'll remember how you tasted.

Summer Recorded

We have a tape recorder that plays slower than it
   should,
gives back the notes of a piano lingering honeyed on
   the air,
guitars as musky fruit from an enchanted wood,
and flutes as tremulous sad maidens bright with golden
   hair;
each sounded moment lasts a fraction longer than the
   beat
of seconds spun out by the clock's unwavering steel.

I have known days like that, of warm winds drowsing
   in the heat
of noon and all of summer spinning slowly on its reel,
days briefly lived, that leave long music in the mind
more sweet than truth; I play them and rewind.

School Buses

You'd think that by the end of June they'd take them-
    selves
Away, get out of sight – but no, they don't; they
Don't at all. You see them waiting through
July in clumps of sumac near the railroad, or
Behind a service station, watching, always watching
    for a
Child who's let go of summer's hand and strayed. I
    have
Seen them hunting on the roads of August – empty
    buses
Scanning woods and ponds with rows of empty eyes.
    This morning
I saw five of them, parked like a week of
Schooldays, smiling slow in orange paint and
Smirking with their mirrors in the sun –
But summer isn't done! Not yet!

Summer Goes

Summer goes, summer goes
Like the sand between my toes
When the waves go out.
That's how summer pulls away,
Leaves me standing here today,
Waiting for the school bus.

Summer brought, summer brought
All the frogs that I have caught,
Frogging at the pond,
Hot dogs, flowers, shells and rocks,
Postcards in my postcard box –
Places far away.

Summer took, summer took
All the lessons in my book,
Blew them far away.
I forgot the things I knew –
Arithmetic and spelling too,
Never thought about them.

Summer's gone, summer's gone –
Fall and winter coming on,
Frosty in the morning.
Here's the school bus right on time.
I'm not really sad that I'm
Going back to school.

My Friend Thelma

Such a friend as my friend Thelma everyone has not.
Such a friend as my friend Thelma is who I have got.

She's the one who always knows
In the winter when it snows
That the school bus will get through,
Calls up kids like me and you
So that we won't think the bus
Isn't coming. Hopeful us.

Thelma, when the ice is new,
Always says, 'I think that you
Ought to try it,' and I do,
And it's thin, and I go through.
When I get home sopping wet,
Into trouble's what I get.

Thelma will drop in on me
When I have friends, two or three,
Playing dolls and having fun.
Thelma is the extra one
Who is there when she should be
Somewhere else and not with me.

I have seen her several times
With an uncle who gives dimes
Going to the movies. They will take
Other friends, and they have cake
Topped with ice-cream after. All good chances
Go to other friends than Frances.

My friend Thelma is a pain but one that I can stay
   with.
I know people who have even worse than her to play
   with.

October Tuesday

One crow in a high wind over Chelsea,
black against a rain sky loops and swings,
writes, *'Black against a rain sky'* with its wings.
One leaf, blown yellowing upward over Paultons
    Square,
writes *'Winter soon, yes, winter'* on the air.

The Sea Gull's Eye

The thing about a gull is not the soaring flight, the
    creaking cry;
The thing about a sea gull is its eye –
Eye of the wind, the ocean's eye, not pretty,
Black at the centre of its yellow stare, no pity
And no fear in it, nor reason, nothing warm
To shelter its own wildness from the storm –
Naked life only, disdainful of its form.

Along the harbour road the other day
I found a broken sea gull where it lay
Great-winged and skyless, wrecked by stone or shot –
Some boy, perhaps, had done it who had not
More pity than his prey
And there it lay
And lived awhile, until that yellow eye
No longer looked out on the ocean sky,
And life, indifferent to boys with stones,
Flew up again with crows that picked the bones.

Typo

'Nitgub,' said the typewriter,
And clenched the paper tight.
'Nitgub positively.
It is here in black and white.'
'Nonsense,' I said.
'I typed N-O-T-H-I-N-G;
The word, of course, was *nothing*,
Simply nothing, don't you see?'
'Nothing may be what you meant,
But *nitgub*'s what you wrote.
I like it,' said the typewriter.
'It strikes a happy note.
It has more style than *nothing*,
Has a different sort of sound.
The colour is superior;
The flavour's nice and round.
Have you plumbed its deepest depths,
Its mystery explained!'
'All right,' I said, 'I'll take it.
Nitgub ventured, nitgub gained.'

Tomorrow Wonders

'What will they bring me, I wonder?'
says Tomorrow, sleepless in the dark,
thirsting for a glass of water,
feeling his pyjamas rumpled, twisted, and awry.
'What will they bring me?'

'Pennies old and green with mould,
silent whistles, knives with broken blades,'
the clock says, cursing.

'Oh, no,' Tomorrow murmurs,
'they will bring me tasselled trumpets,
kites and oranges, copper horses, sugared owls,
dragons of gingerbread with yellow raisin eyes.'

'Don't,' the clock says, striking
BONG BONG BONG, 'don't,' the clock says,
'count on it.'

At Dimla

At Dimla when the moon was new
the streets were dark, their hopes were few.

At Dimla when they beat the drum
they hoped that nothing bad would come.

At Dimla when they sang the song
they tried to sing it not too long.

At Dimla when they barred the gate
they found they'd left it much too late
at Dimla.

The Rendezvous at Zarmni

The dark ones came and the ones from the sea,
the mountain ones and the great unshapens, all came to
Zarmni with the spring tides in the dark of the moon, all
came to Zarmni in the dark of the moon.

The ones who knew one word, the ones who knew
two and three, the ones with a sign or a gesture or
wearing a sigil, the ones who wept for the grass, sang
for the bone, scanned all the line of the
long, long ebbtide, walking like birds, birding their
thoughts of the sea at Zarmni.

And the ruins! The wind, how it sang on the stones,
  sighed
on the rubble, drummed on the wrecks that lay
stranded where the birds ran incessantly crying on the
tideline while other birds rose continually on the
rising air, continually spreading the slanting circles of
their thought, themselves the thoughts of the wind that
blurred the lights of the coast, lights at sea,
seen lights and unseen at Zarmni.

And the dogs on the strand, the dogs like shadows, like
darkness that runs on four legs, the dogs
running silent between long rows of dead lamps on
the broken esplanade at Zarmni.
Strange oracles, strange timepieces, stone flutes,
bone whistles, drums in the smoke and the light of the
watchfires, and the auguries were good; all read the
auguries and they were good at Zarmni.

The auguries were good. And yet
when it came from the sea, when it parted the
fathomless waters, parted the air above them,
    darkened
the stars, swallowed the silence and did what it did
at Zarmni, no one was surprised.

The Crow

Flying loose and easy, where does he go
Swaggering in the sky, what does he know,
Why is he laughing, the carrion crow?
Why is he shouting, why won't he sing,
How did he steal them, whom will he bring
Loaves of blue heaven under each wing?

The Sparrow Hawk

Wings like pistols flashing at his sides,
Masked, above the meadow runway rides,
Galloping, galloping with an easy rein.
Below, the fieldmouse, where the shadow glides,
Holds fast the small purse of his life, and hides.

What the Wind Said

'Far away is where I've come from,' said the wind
'Guess what I've brought you.'
   'What?' I asked.
'Shadows dancing on a brown road by an old
Stone fence,' the wind said. 'Do you like that?'
   'Yes,' I said. 'What else?'
'Daisies nodding, and the drone of one small airplane
In a sleepy sky,' the wind continued.
   'I like the airplane, and the daisies too,' I said.
   'What else!'
'That's not enough?' the wind complained.
   'No,' I said. 'I want the song that you were singing.
   Give me that.'
'That's mine,' the wind said. 'Find your own.' And left.

To Walter de la Mare
1873–1956

His words in pasture safely sing
With grazing sheep,
Or dark in owl-lit belfry swing
Where demons sleep;
And sometimes like Great Paul they ring
With hugely quivering bronze to bring
Bright angels standing on each roof,
And to each window startled truth.

BRIAN LEE

Brian Lee was born in July 1935 in Ealing, west London, and spent his first five years there, moving to Edinburgh when the war broke out. He was educated at Drayton Manor Grammar School, Ealing. He left there to serve his national service with the RAF in England and West Germany, returning to become a journalist on local newspapers in west London and Buckinghamshire and on the *Aberdeen Press and Journal.*

He read English at University College, London, followed by an education year at Leeds University. Later he studied at Edinburgh University. He has worked as a teacher of English to craft apprentices, technical and engineering students, and students of English Literature at Newcastle Polytechnic.

His publications are miscellaneous. He has written poetry for children (*Late Home*, Kestrel Books, 1976) and adults, including satirical poetry published in many magazines and as a collection (*In English*, HQ Press, 1974). He edited the *Haltwhistle Quarterly* with Duke Maskell from 1973 to 1983 and contributed critical articles on literature, education and language to a wide range of magazines. He has written pamphlets on the state of English teaching (*Poetry and the System*, Brynmill Press, 1983 and *The Dislocation of Everyday Life*, Brynmill Press, 1988) and a study of T. S. Eliot's literary criticism (*Theory and Personality*, Athlone Press, 1979).

The selection in *Six of the Best* is taken from *Late Home*, poems published in various anthologies and unpublished work, some of which have been broadcast on BBC Radio for Schools.

Brian Lee wasn't keen on poetry (or anything much) at school. Books used for exams and lessons seemed different from those he enjoyed at home – *Treasure Island*, *The Pickwick Papers*, *Tom Brown's Schooldays* – and one poetry book he still remembers, *A Poetry Book for Boys*, full of stirring 'masculine' verse by Sir Walter Scott, Kipling, Henry Newbolt and Macaulay. Even in the 1950s modern poetry was hardly mentioned at school, except by one teacher, with a curious, dainty habit of crooking her finger when she entered marks in the register, who occasionally referred to Edith Sitwell and T. S. Eliot.

It was perhaps these clues that Brian Lee took up when exams were finished and he felt he 'needed' to read. From then on he scarcely stopped, and recalls driving in an RAF lorry to a radar site in the Weser marshes during his national service, his nose always buried in a book. It would probably have been a Penguin Poets edition of T. S. Eliot, Stephen Spender, W. H. Auden or C. Day Lewis. Then he began to write, usually in the style of the last person he had read.

Later on, as a journalist (still reading, on the Green Line coach this time, off to a flower show or council meeting), he tore his writing up – he knew how bad it was. At the age of twenty-five he became a student at University College, London, met teachers and students whose main conversation was about literature, and began to find his bearings. When he was twenty-six, he wrote the first poem he didn't throw away.

Poetry for children came later, as a way of expressing

intimate memories, the personal experience that lies underneath grown-up experience, as a way of finding an audience that would demand something readable, clear and honest, and might allow you to do something that wasn't just for children. He has always been a great admirer of Walter de la Mare, and had in fact been re-reading the collection *Peacock Pie* while invigilating some examinations the day before we met. His favourite poem in it is 'The Song of the Mad Prince', though he thinks that 'The Bookworm' might well be him:

> 'Something has gone, and ink and print
>   Will never bring it back;
> I long for the green fields again,
>   I'm tired of books,' said Jack.

Among other writers for and about children he admires Wordsworth, Blake, Dickens, Stevenson, William Soutar, Mark Twain and Eliot.

Today Brian is a senior lecturer in English Literature at Newcastle Polytechnic. His wife Chris (formerly a children's librarian) is a teacher, and they have four children, Thomas, James, Mary and Peter. Thomas has been known to call his father 'the best poet in the world'.

Brian's own childhood was disrupted by the Second World War. His father went away to war, leaving his son, an only child, in the company of women and older people, his mother, aunt, grandparents. Perhaps they communicated some of their wartime fears to him when they took him away from the London blitz to the safety of Edinburgh. His poems often explore the experience of a timid small boy bravely trying to keep up with the others, to be, as the last line of 'The Tunnel' states: 'One of the gang.' He writes realistically about those bad moments of childhood – waking at night, fear of the unknown, boredom, loneliness, the guilt of disobedience. A young Canadian boy, after reading 'Late Home', said, 'I've felt like that!' and Brian says that's one of the best bits of criticism he's had!

During the war Brian would watch trains by the hour: troop trains, goods trains, local trains, always on the look out:

> for the one that would bring me
> someone much taller than I remembered
> and his voice much stronger,
> in his uniform like a stranger
> to be there, back from the war.

He remembers being taken when he was seven by steam train to Aberdour to watch the war ships on the Firth of Forth. The train was called after a character in a Scott novel, Peter Poundtext, and there were other romantically named trains too – Lady of Avenel, Rhoderick Dhu, Jingling Geordie. The countryside and dialect of Scotland got into his blood, as well as its trains: he calls himself a 'steam-engine freak'. His poem 'On the Platform' shows his feeling for trains, and he hopes to work these experiences into more poems.

Back in the South after the war, Brian Lee lived and went to school near to where I live in Ealing, west London. He was therefore familiar with a local landmark, the bridge built by the famous Brunel, and the trains going to Paddington, or to the West Country.

Reading through Brian's poems you are strongly

aware of him as an observer, a looker-on, a listener; he
has stored in his memory what he once saw and heard.
That night watchman at the end of an Edinburgh street
in the forties will never know that the inquisitive boy
grew up to put him in a poem called 'The Watchman'!

Nowadays Brian's life is firmly based in north Tyneside
with his work and family. In any spare time he gets
(and that's not much with four young children), he likes
'walking, thinking, playing the piano'.

I asked what he would say to young people experiment-
ing with writing poetry, and his answer was: 'To
recognize it as the best possible expression of their experiences.'

Late Home

I looked up – the sun had gone down
Though it was there a minute before
And the light had grown terribly thin
And no one played by the shore
Of the lake, now empty, and still;
And I heard the park-keepers shout
As they cycled around the paths . . .
'Closing, closing . . . everyone out . . .'

Then I panicked and started to run,
Leaving all of my friends behind
(I could hear their cries in the bushes –
It was me they were trying to find)
But they had the burn and the minnows,
The rope, the slide, the shrubbery track,
And the trees where a thrush was singing,
And I had the long road back –

The road that led, empty and straight,
Down under the tall grey flats
Where the lights were on, and the tellies,
And old ladies were putting out cats:
I ran past them, without looking round
As though I'd committed a crime:
At six they'd said 'Just half an hour'
And *now* – oh, what was the time?

How could it have gone already?
Something must be, it *must* be, wrong –
I've only just come out – and why

Does getting back take me so long?
I can't be late – or if I am,
It's the fault of the sun or the moon.
When the dentist's takes an eternity,
How are happy things over so soon?

So I stopped and asked, 'Please mister . . .'
And his left wrist came slowly round
And he peered at his watch and shook it
And said 'Blast, it's never been wound.'
But the next man hauled his watch up,
Like a lead sinker on a line,
Clicked open the front, and boomed out,
'Right now, child, it's five to nine.'

There's a great big gap in between
The way things are, the way things seem,
And I dropped down it then, like you do
When you shoot back to life from a dream.
I stood there and muttered 'It can't be –
His watch must be wrong' – then, aghast –
'This time, I'll *really* be for it,
If it isn't a whole two hours fast.'

But I got my legs going again
And ran, gulping in red-hot air,
Through back-streets where no one knew me,
Till I came out in the Town Square.
But when I looked at the shining face
And I heard the cheerful chimes
Of the Town Hall clock – then every hope
Drained away, as it struck nine times.

Two hours late . . . two hours late –
Perhaps they've called out the police
Two hours late . . . who, all in a line,
Are combing the waste ground, piece by piece;
While *they* all stand in our window
Anxious and angry and, when I'm seen,
Ready to frown and shout 'There he is',
'Come here you!', and 'Where's the child been?'

When I come round the corner and see them,
I'll limp, as though I'd a sprain,
Then whimper 'I didn't mean it' and
'I'll never ever go out, again . . .
How can I know that time's up,
When I'm enjoying myself such a lot?
I'm sorry – won't you take me back in?
Are you glad to see me, or not?'

. . . But later in bed, as I lay there
In the extraordinary light –
Filtering through the half-drawn curtain –
Of that silvery spellbound night,
I wondered just what *had* happened
To Time, for three hours in June:
If all of my life is as happy –
Will it all be over as soon?

Night Music

1

The mail train south fades out into the dark.
The clock ticks, tocks, downstairs in the hall.
Conversations come in murmurs through the wall.
The dog barks once that only gives one bark.
The leaves are rustling all around the empty park.

The staircase creaks, as though somebody was there.
Dad's bike ticks down the path; the shed doors close.
Knocking: floorboards groan: mutters of radios.
Someone clears his throat – a match scrapes, to flare
Where fat moths whirl in the wheezy streetlamp's
    glare.

Starlings scuffle, scuffle, underneath the roof.
Car-doors slam, slam, slam; two church-clocks chime.
A call – 'Sssh!' Whispers. 'Will you?' 'Yes.' 'What
    time?'
Cats hiss and spit; a dustbin-lid comes off.
Out of the damp fields, comes a hoarse cow-cough.

A door clicks; and swishes open, on its own . . .
Milk-bottles tinkle on a step. A window shrieks
Upwards; the bath-tap whispers as it leaks . . .

And always there, behind, a ceaseless monotone,
The steady stir, the sound of everyone.

2

. . . And beyond this, everywhere,
Are all the things I cannot hear:
Fieldmice chipping at an ear
Of swaying corn, the steady whirr
Of rabbits mowing grass, the roar
Of woodworm in the furniture;
Hedgehog-grunts, the nightjar's hover,
Midge-squeaks, bat-squeal, cockroach-purr,
The leathery creak of a chrysalis;
Buzz, whines, drones, a scream, the hiss
Of adders moving – badgers' snores,
The pad, pad, pad, of the foxes' paws:

– A swishing, as the centipede
Sweeps himself along, full-speed;
Scrapings, as a fat house-fly
Rubs his hands, at a crumb of pie;
The beetle, to some burial-place
Rattling away, a hardened case;
There, the steady electric hum
Of slugs travelling on their own slime;
And juicy *crunches*, down black holes
Where worms are turned into black moles;
A pad, pad, pad, of the foxes' paws,
Visiting chickens, in a good cause.

– Each creature, that will always be
Itself alone, and strange to me.

3

. . . And far beyond this,
Up there, where next
To nothing is,
Which if I think
For long about
My mind goes blank;
Among the cease-
less seethe
Of galaxies,
Of stars, where each
Keeps to its place:

Is there, for each,
One special note
My human ear
's too dull to hear,
Its singular voice
Adding to all –
A harmony
Inaudible,
That sounds

In soundless space

?

In the Green Shade

I wade by the edge of the sparkling stream
Plunged waist-down in a sea of green
The still spread of dock and wild-rhubarb leaves
I can push to one side and peek between

At another world, where the half-light is green
And the stiff stalks and the arching leaves
Make cloisters I almost could crawl between
On the damp dark earth that slopes to the stream.

What would it be like to live under the leaves
The sunlight never filters between?
To slide like a snail, silent, leaving a stream
Of moisture behind me, white on the green?

To be one of the slug-herd, and creep in between
My shiny brethren, moo down to the stream,
And drink in the dark, or be one of the green
Bat-insects that hang upside-down from the leaves?

I shiver, and stand. The once-sparkling stream
Runs grey under trees no longer so green
For the sun has gone that shone through their leaves
And a chill wind has drawn black clouds in between.

Cold Feet

They have all gone across
They are all turning to see
They are all shouting 'come on'
They are all waiting for me.

I look through the gaps in the footway
And my heart shrivels with fear,
For far below the river is flowing
So quick and so cold and so clear.

And all that there is between it
And me falling down there is this:
A few wooden planks – not very thick –
And between each, a little abyss.

The holes get right under my sandals.
I can see straight through to the rocks,
And if I don't look, I can feel it,
Just there, through my shoes and my socks.

Suppose my feet and my legs withered up
And slipped through the slats like a rug?
Suppose I suddenly went very thin
Like the baby that slid down the plug?

I know that it cannot happen
But suppose that it did, what then?
Would they be able to find me
And take me back home again?

They have all gone across
They are all waiting to see
They are all shouting 'come on' –
But they'll have to carry me.

The Tunnel

This is the way that I have to go
I've left all my friends behind
Back there, where a faint light glimmers
Round the long tunnel's bend.

I can't see a roof up above me,
I can't find either wall,
My shoes slip on the slimy boulders –
How far is it down, if I fall?

Beneath me the same stream is flowing
That laughed in the fields back there –
Here, it is black, like the leeches and weeds,
And the bats flitting through the dank air.

It's just the same if I shut my eyes:
My companions, all around,
Are trickles, drips, sploshes, sudden *plops*,
Then, a strange, sucking sound.

One shoe's full of the cold dark water,
My hands slither over the stones,
My throat's gone dry, my heart pound-pounds,
But I can only go on –

Till I can see them, they can see me
And again they start to shout,
The rats bite, watch out for the rats,
But now I am almost out:

Dizzy, happy, I blink at the light,
The sun's still shining, the birds still sing.
Someone is patting me on the back –
Now I am one of the gang.

Bobby Charlton

like this: head up, looking where he was going
just as you were supposed to, but always
changing direction, slightly, now this
way, now that, no more than needed so that
obstructions do not have to be met
are not there, simply:
                              a kind of cunning
for a shy man, nothing as artless as contact,
evasion was mannerly:
                              head up,
knowing where he was, where the others were
what they were doing, and changing the pattern
with the same flowing unhastening stride:
head up, shoulders back, leaning from the toes,
the same stride with the conscious grace gone
that used to bring him bending in from his wing,
faded into something better, at the centre, experienced
making connections from such a distance . . .

Confluence, influence, with the same flow, although
older, slower, the moments were fewer;
one of the best, and better than some of the best,
as good as he could be, and then at last
a refinement of all that he had been: like that.

Eric

Outside, a steely sky and plate
Of trodden two-months' snow
Cover the playground, and the fields
That reach up from the railway
And climb to the estate;
A surviving crow
Tugs at a shred of vegetation.

Inside in the warm, the other eight
Keep turning round
As if this was the way to find
And trap, one word
Of all the words that come and go,
The answer that will make the question let them go –
At times their eyes light up with what they find.

Last evening you came to me, lost
Because you had lost a shilling,
Face frozen past
Tears you had not wept:
The whole world crossed
You, till I gave you a shilling.

Today you smile your thanks simply
At the desks, the walls, the others,
Blank paper, blank snow
And teacher, who does not know
What's best for you,
Who would like to give you more shillings.

New Shoes

I keep close to walls –
I go the back way –
They made me wear my
Stiff heavy best new
Shoes to school today.

They can't understand it,
I shouldn't be so silly –
But my old ones have got holes in
Or I'd never put these on:
They're just not *me*.

In my desk I sit with them
Tucked under my seat,
These big, bright, boat-size
Brand-new brogues I don't
Want anyone to meet.

– Such as our Miss Wilkins
Who'd look twice and say
As she goes past: 'My, my –
*Some*one's got some nice
New yellow shoes on today.'

I'm hiding in the cloakrooms
(No one's noticed yet),
With my feet under the benches . . .
I *won't* go out,
I'm trying to forget . . .

Like marble pedestals
They fix me to the spot.
Everywhere, I'm caught
In the act of wearing them,
Guilty, though I'm not.

Now I'm standing in the long grass
All on my own.
– I'd sooner have
The Emperor's
New clothes on.

Hot and Cold

Everybody all excited and hot,
the candles had just been blown out,
we'd had Hunt the Thimble, and Forfeits, and It,
Postman's Knock, Murders, and Musical Chairs
and Sardines in the broom-cupboard under the stairs;
there was the smell of hot wax and crackers just
    pulled,
and the table was a mountain of food;
everyone was sitting with paper hats on,
and voices were saying 'Oh, good',
'I'm having *that*' and 'All that's mine',
and ''tisn't' and ''tis' and 'just see',
and the hot pies were getting near me;
when, in the peace that means mouths are full,
and you all look forward to what's coming next –
cake, and pastries, and jelly, and ice –
I noticed the boy sitting opposite me,
and what he was doing was not very nice:
so I told him what I had been told
(I forget what it was now, maybe
'Don't suck when you drink,' or 'Don't pick your
    nose' –
it was only what I had been told);
and the silence suddenly froze
except for a voice that said '*Well!* –'
like the end-of-break bell,
'*that*'s not very nice,'
and whoever said it was hushed
as I went very cold

at the very same moment I blushed:
my face like a furnace, my backbone like ice.

Every face round the table turned where I was
like a creature with forty-eight eyes,
all wide, all round, all looking in
to the silence they made, like a clear solid block,
with me inside of it, stuck:
and all you could hear was the clock:
tick, tock.

Twenty-four jaws never chewed.
Three adults just stood.
I felt as though I'd gone nude
on an empty moor, with the wind very strong,
and the moment stretched on and stretched on
while the silence went down and went down
and everything said: YOU'RE WRONG,
YOU'RE WRONG, YOU'RE WRONG, YOU'VE
    GOT SOMETHING WRONG.

– O what had I done?

I'd only told him what I had been told –
and I know what it was, to tell you the truth:
'Don't talk with your mouth full, *we* don't want to see:
it's all going around like a washing-machine,
you ought to know better, you're older than me.'
It might have been '*Don't*
take the biggest one,' or
'*Will* you stop picking that sore,'
'It's very bad manners to *ask* for some more,'
'If you wipe your nose on your sleeve then we won't

take you with us, we've told you before' –
I know all of it, well enough,
But now there is something else that I don't.

I'd like to go home now, not sit
behind all this stuff I don't want to eat,
keeping my face in my plate
and wishing that I could slide
myself into a hot pie's inside,
and hide.
So long as I'm here I'm out in the cold.
There's something I need to be told.

– I could almost crawl under the table and cry.

I wish I could die.

Rain

The lights are all on, though it's just past midday,
There are no more indoor games we can play,
No one can think of anything to say,
It rained all yesterday, it's raining today,
It's grey outside, inside me it's grey.

I stare out of the window, fist under my chin,
The gutter leaks drips on the lid of the dustbin,
When they say 'cheer up', I manage a grin,
I draw a fish on the glass with a sail-sized fin,
It's sodden outside, and it's damp within.

Matches, bubbles and papers pour into the drains,
Clouds smother the sad laments from the trains,
Grandad says it brings on his rheumatic pains,
The moisture's got right inside of my brains,
It's raining outside, inside me it rains.

Our Bonfire

Our bonfire still smoulders as we start back for home,
The blue woodsmoke floats straight to the sky
Wafting feathers of ash from the foot of the hollow
That's hidden from everyone's eye.

The heat on our cheeks! The spark and the spit!
The cracklings, the smart of the smoke! –
Dwindling down now to nothing, grey-gentle as down,
Where we snuggled our taties to cook.

The sun slides down, the long night will be cold,
But I'll think, when I'm tucked up in bed,
Of somebody sleeping, secret and warm, where today
Our rotten beechboughs blazed red.

Smoke in our nostrils, and smoke on our tongues,
Ash on our eyelids, our clothes and our hair –
As, smelling all kippered, we saunter to tea:
And trouble, but none of us care.

The Watchman

Have you ever spent hours on a cold Saturday
When street-lamps grow haloes and cars *hiss* away,
With a misty moon floating, and frost drawing in,
When the pub lights come on, as the shops start to
    shut –
Just watching the watchman just sit, in his hut?

He's bent over the Pink'un in an oil-stained old mac
And a cap and mittens, his boots glassy-black;
He lights up his pipe, stretches, drifts off in a doze,
While there by the doorway, to keep the night out,
Steams a fat round kettle, sooted up to the spout,

On the oil-drum brazier, blazing into the air,
Its flames licking out in a wavery glare –
Like colour gone solid, it's pure scarlet all through . . .
When the lid lifts and rattles, he stumps from his fug
With a tin plate and irons, and a chipped brown mug,

To fit his fork up with bacon, which sizzles and curls
To a quintessence of crispness packed into two rolls
Running with butter, his red tongue scoops round . . .
Then at last, with a wink, makes a wide open door
To come into the country where he is the Law.

Then you sit on sack cushions in his close wooden cell
And trim up a wick, in the paraffin-smell,
And hear what he has to say of the world –
That's not what it was – of increases in crime,
A two-to-one treble, politicians, and Time

That flies – as you fetch him some thingumabob,
Take a sip at his mug, and think, *What a Job!*:
To read, and consider . . . the nature of things . . .
Have you ever done that, on cold Saturdays,
When frost grows on roofs, the moon floats in a haze?

The Man Who Wasn't There

Yesterday upon the stair
I met the man who wasn't there;
He wasn't there again today,
I wish, I wish, he'd go away.

I've seen his shapeless shadow-coat
Beneath the stairway, hanging about;
And outside, muffled in a cloak
The same colour as the dark;

I've seen him in a black, black suit
Shaking, under the broken light;
I've seen him swim across the floor
And disappear beneath the door;

And once, I almost heard his breath
Behind me, running up the path:
Inside, he leant against the wall,
And turned . . . and was no one at all.

Yesterday upon the stair,
I met the man who wasn't there;
He wasn't there again today,
I wish, I wish, he'd go away.

Empty Fears

What's that? – Coming after me, down the street,
With the sound of somebody dragging one foot
Behind him, who pauses, who watches, who goes
With a shuffle and mutter
From the wall to the gutter
In the patch where the light from the lamps doesn't
    meet . . .

Oh . . . it's only a bit of paper – a hollow brown bag
Open-mouthed, like a shout – a bit like the face
Crumpled-up, of someone who's going to cry,
Blown on the wind, from place to place,
Pointless, and light, and dry.

Who's that? – Watching, from the upstairs windows
Of the house where the hedge grows right back to the
    door,
Where the half-drawn curtains droop and discolour
And a yellow bulb burns away
And the milk's on the step all day –
Somebody lives there, no one comes or goes . . .

Oh . . . it's only an empty coat on a hanger
That sways in a draught like a man who depends
On only one thing – the something inside
That's holding him up, waiting for friends
He writes to, but no one's replied.

What's that? – Whispering, where the fence round the lot
Sags like a fading hope: the gate just here twists

On its hinge like a bird's broken wing
And shrieks as you look, and see:
Nothing, where all the shops used to be,
People coming and going where now they are not . . .

Oh . . . it's only the breeze, that's fretting itself
Amongst the stiff thistles, each standing alone,
Upright, all winter, dead, but not gone . . .

But if it's only these things, what blows
Through me, to make me afraid, who knows?

On the Platform

The distance swims in the heat where the rails reach
  far to the South.
To the North thick smoke swirls from the black
  tunnel-mouth.
The sun sucks the scent from the wallflower-beds on
  the platform.
The sleepers leak tar and the fence oozes gum,
smelling of pine, I sniff from my thumb;
coal-smoke mingles with bacon that fries on the
  signalman's stove.
A skylark climbs trilling, and drops,
climbs, and then stops.
A hawk hangs still above the fields by the farm.
Then *ping-ping, ping-ping*;
a swish, the signal-wires shake, with a *clunk*,
the home, and the distant, flops,
the silence settles again, then the rails start to drum.
Nearer and nearer towards me out of the distance
  gathers the terrible threat
that I come here to run from, back from the edge of
  the platform,
cling tight to my seat,
and wait,
until,
with a scream, like a punch in the stomach the train
  whams straight through,
people talking and drinking and reading and walking
  and sleeping and sitting (quite still)
– swallowed up in the black, all gone,
leaving the dust and the papers to settle again,

the seat shaking, and me,
wanting it all to happen again,
asking oh where did they come from, where have they
  gone?

Reflections

The windows in our street
Look at me, as I pass;
And often, I stand and peer
Through myself on the glass,

Through lace and velvets, in
To bits of someone else's life –
A table, laid; a flickering fire,
Vases, palms, a jewelled knife,

The old lady playing hymns alone,
A party I am nearly at,
The macaw sitting looking bored,
Sunlight on a sleeping cat;

Fading photos, roses, brass . . .
The different things . . . that lie
Just out of reach, beyond the panes
That mix me and them and street and sky.

And in every one of them
Something is going on;
Something that started years ago,
Joys, or troubles, come or gone . . .

I stand there, imagining
So many likelihoods unwind,
Endlessly inward, taking me
With them, silently, behind

The windows that watch me
Like eyes, from their confine –
As I look into yours,
As you look into mine.

I Am

In the chill church –
empty pews,
the musty smell
of things that had once been new,

winter light filtering in
down at the front
stained by the dark glass
beside the font.

Some of us sat, some stood
like sheep in a fold
huddled together
against the cold –

Grandma and the cousins
his father and mother
lots of uncles, aunts,
a sister, two brothers;

the young and the old
enclosing among
them two others,
one old and one young,

one speaking old words
to a tiny fresh face
asleep in the midst
of that ancient place

and the ancient occasion
for him, all alone
in the arms of a Father
who was not his own.

But when the cold water
was poured over his head;
and the sign was made,
and the words were said . . .

he did not cry,
who now had his name,
for the rest of his life
to be: never the same.

And we all gave a sigh
of relief, and smiled,
with the warmth of summer
on this new child,

in the arms of his Mother
(Grandma whispered 'the lamb') –
only the words were missing
to say 'I am'.

On Christmas Eve

On Christmas Eve, the three of us –
as if it was something we wanted to do,
without anyone saying *it's got to be done* –
cleaned out our rabbit, its bed and its run.

Jamie held Nibbles, because she is his,
as if he was a grown-up, the rabbit a child,
whispering things, and stroking one ear,
saying 'there now darling', it wasn't to fear, –

while Mary just watched, because she's so young
(except for our Peter, he can't even walk),
though she did do the things I asked her to
without answering back, or starting to argue . . .

So I did the worst of it (my name is Tom)
scraping old mash, and chewed stalks, and crusts,
wet sawdust and, well, you know what I mean
into the dustbin, then I swept the yard clean.

– We did it together, the three of us;
and none of us minded, and no one had asked,
or said if we didn't, *that rabbit must go* . . .
and why were we so good . . .? I don't know.

We put Nibbles back, and all three said Goodnight,
and went for our bath, leaving everything nice,
with a carrot, some mash, the end off the bread,
and lots of sweet hay, to lay down her head.

Noman's Land

Don't you go out tonight –
I won't go out tonight:
What whispered like leaves in the ditch by the road?
What creaked, like loose boards, in the empty old
house?
What swelled, like a cloak, from the edge of the wood,
As the dark grew thicker when the trees were blown
close?
– When something pushed me,
Something brushed me,
Something touched me – again, and again:
In Noman's Land,
In Noman's Land,
Between
Where you are going, and where you have been.

Don't you go out tonight –
I won't go out tonight:
What flapped like wet raincoats, far out in the field?
What shapes came and went in the alleyway's mist?
What coughed in the culvert, inside, where the cold
Burn water went through the black gratings so fast?
– When something nipped me,
Something tripped me,
Something gripped me – again and again:
In Noman's Land,
In Noman's Land,
Between
Where you are going, and where you have been.

Sad . . . and Glad

The sun has gone down,
Leaving an empty sky
Above the moor
Above our town.
Street-lights switch on.
Buses *swish* by.
Strangers are laughing,
My friends have gone in:
I'm alone –
It's time to go home.

Someone runs to the post,
Leaving an open door –
A family
Makes itself toast
Round the fire
Down a long corridor.
It's chilly now,
And I've been out all day.
I want my tea.
It's time I was home.

They're calling a William,
Leaving me wishing I'm him . . .
On the allotments
Bonfire smoke rolls
Sluggish, grey.
I'm still streets away:
This time of year,
This time of day,
Makes me sad –
And glad, to get home.

Index of First Lines

234

Acknowledgements

The editor and publishers gratefully acknowledge kind permission to reproduce the following copyright poems in this book:

Faber and Faber Ltd for all the poems included here by George Barker; Century Hutchinson Ltd for 'Before The Game' and 'Fire Drill' from *The Old Flea-Pit* by Alan Brownjohn; Dobson Books Ltd for 'In March', 'First Primrose', 'The Beach', 'Button Box' and 'August Ends' from *Good Company*, 'Singing in the Streets' from *Singing in the Streets* and 'Montana Born' and 'The President' from *The Broad Atlantic*, all by Leonard Clark. Faber and Faber Ltd for a six-line extract from 'To the Memory of Walter de la Mare 1873–1956' from *Collected Poems 1909–1962* by T. S. Eliot.